A Manual of Mechanical Movements

A MANUAL OF
Mechanical Movements

EDITED BY
Will M. Clark

Garden City Publishing Company, Inc.
GARDEN CITY, NEW YORK

CL

PRINTED IN THE UNITED STATES OF AMERICA

Foreword

THE SIMPLEST as well as the most complicated machines, varying in complexity from the patent can-opener to the range-finder of one hundred thousand moving parts, perform their work by integrating fundamental mechanical movements. The can-opener may involve only a gear and lever mechanism and the range-finder hundreds of developed reciprocal, alternating and oscillatory movements, but the components are similar and based on the same rudimentary principles.

This manual attempts to describe these rudimentary principles and trace their development in application.

The material in Part One originally appeared in a publication called THE AMERICAN ARTISAN, which had its brief day about the middle of the last century, and was chosen as representing, with the clarity of uncomplicated youth, the childhood, or at most adolescence, of the machine age. It is difficult to take a modern automobile or similar complicated present-day machine apart and analyze the principles of leverage and motion that make it tick, but these principles are in themselves simple and the machine merely represents a coordination of fundamental movements such as are described in the following pages. The editor chooses to build rather than to dissect.

In a sense, Part Two represents the culmination of a life-long hobby. In it the reader will find photographs of a collection of working models which set forth in tangible form the application of the principles described in Part One. The exhibit is the editor's own creation—lock, stock, and barrel—and he regards it with pardonable pride. It has been on view at expositions and museums throughout the country and has been received by literally millions with flattering acclaim.

v

It is hoped that this manual will make for a clearer understanding of machines by those who operate them, and bring to them the feeling that a machine is a living thing of many articulated parts, each performing its own particular task in turning out its product.

WILL M. CLARK

Glossary of Terms

BEARING A part on which a pivot, pin, or the like, turns or revolves.

BEVEL GEARS Those which have grooves not at right angles to the shaft.

CAM Rotating or sliding piece or projection, as on a wheel, for moving or receiving from a roller, pin, or the like, motion against its edge.

CENTRIFUGAL FORCE Force directed outward from the center when a body is made to move in a curved path.

CLUTCH Mechanical device used to connect a driving and a driven member on the same axis.

COMBUSTION The act of burning.

COUNTERSHAFT Intermediate shaft for receiving or transmitting motion, sometimes called a jack shaft.

CRANK A part or arm at right angles to a shaft to receive or impart motion.

DEVICE Refers to an ingenious machine.

DISC Flat circular plate.

DRUM A cylindrical part of a machine resembling the musical instrument of this name.

DYNAMOMETER Apparatus for measuring force.

ECCENTRIC A revolving disc having the point on which it revolves off the center of the disc.

ELLIPTIC GEARS Those having the form of an ellipse.

EPICYCLIC TRAIN A train of gears or pulleys constrained to move bodily around the circumference of another gear or pulley.

ESCAPEMENT A mechanism in which a toothed wheel acts upon two distinct pieces or pallets attached to a reciprocating frame.

FLANGE In this case a rim for a guide to another object.

FORCE A push or pull. Any action between two bodies which changes, or tends to change their relative condition as to rest, motion, or other physical interrelation.

FRICTION A resistance or force which opposes every effort to slide or roll one body over another.

GEAR A mechanical part by which motion is transmitted in machinery.

GENERATE To produce. Used here in the sense of producing power to do certain work.

GOVERNOR Automatic attachment to a machine for controlling its speed.

GRAVITY A force or pull which attracts bodies to the center of the earth.

HYDRAULIC MECHANISMS Those operated or effected by water.

INCLINED PLANE A simple machine for overcoming work. One of the basic principles of mechanics.

INERTIA A property of matter by which it tends to remain in motion if in motion, or at rest if at rest, unless acted upon by some external force.

INTERMITTENT MOTION Periodic; coming and going at intervals; alternate.

JOINT A connection link for transmitting power between two shafts.

LEVER A simple machine. One of the basic principles of mechanics.

LEVERAGE Action of a lever or the mechanical advantage gained by a lever.

MACHINE A combination of mechanical parts which serve to transmit and multiply force and motion so as to do work.

MECHANICAL ADVANTAGE In a machine it is multiplying power.

MESHING OF GEARS Engagement of the teeth of the driving gear with the driven gear.

MITER GEARS Those with grooves at an angle of 45° to the shaft.

MUTILATED GEARS Those with an incomplete circle on teeth.

OSCILLATING MOTION Swinging or moving back and forth over a field.

PALLET Teeth on an escapement mechanism which alternately engage with the teeth of the toothed wheel.

PAWL An arm which falls into the notches of a ratchet wheel to permit motion in one direction only.

PENDULUM A body suspended from a fixed point so that it may swing freely to and fro.

PINION Cogwheel with a small number of teeth designed to mesh with a larger wheel or rack.

PISTON Close-fitting piece which slides within a cylinder.

PISTON ROD Rod which connects the piston with the crank shaft.

PITMAN ROD Rod which connects any driving member in a machine to its driven member.

PLATEN Roller of a typewriter against which the paper rests to be printed.

POWER The rate of doing work.

PULLEY A simple machine. A wheel used to transmit power by means of a band, belt, etc.

PUMP A machine for lifting, compressing, or transferring liquids or gases.

QUADRANT   An area equal to one quarter of a circle.

RADIAL ENGINE   An engine with its cylinders diverging from the crank shaft placed in center.

RATCHET   A mechanism composed of a toothed wheel which is turned in one direction by an arm called a pawl.

RECIPROCATING MOTION   Movement backwards and forwards.

RECTILINEAR MOTION   Motion in a straight line.

REVERSE MOTION   Opposite, contrary, or turned-back motion.

ROTARY MOTION   Motion which turns as a wheel on its axis.

SCREW   A simple machine. An inclined plane wrapped around a cylinder.

SCREW PROPELLER   A form of screw for pushing or pulling a body through air or water.

SCROLL GEARS   Those which, because of their form, produce a gradual increase and decrease of speed during one revolution.

SHAFT   A bar to support rotating parts or to transmit power by turning.

SHEAVE   Grooved wheel of a pulley.

SPRING   Elastic body or device which recovers its original shape when released after being distorted.

SPROCKET WHEEL   A toothed wheel shaped to engage with a chain.

SPUR GEARS   Those having grooves parallel to the shaft.

STEAM ENGINE   An engine driven or worked by steam.

STUD   Short projecting rod or pin on a mechanism for giving or receiving motion against its edge.

TRAIN OF MECHANISMS   Series of connected mechanisms.

TRANSMISSION OF MOTION   Act of passing on motion from the driver to the driven member of a machine.

TREADLE A lever device pressed by the foot to operate a machine.

TURBINE Rotary motor, operated by the force of water or steam against its curved vanes.

UNIVERSAL JOINT Flexible joint which allows variation in the angle between the two shafts.

VACUUM Space where there is literally nothing.

VALVE A device which regulates the direction of the flow of a liquid or gas or shuts it off.

WEDGE A simple machine. Another form of the inclined plane.

WORK The act of a force upon a body causing it to move.

WORM A continuous screw.

YOKE Frame in which a particular part of a machine works.

Contents

PART ONE

A Manual of Mechanical Movements

I.

Fundamentals in Mechanical Movement

1. PULLEYS

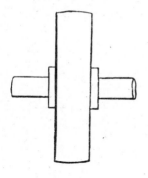

No. 1

A plain pulley for a flat belt crowned for centering.

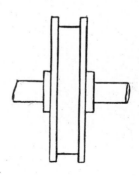

No. 3

A flanged pulley to drive or be driven by a flat belt.

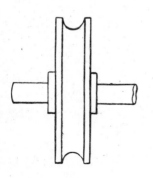

No. 2

A concave-grooved pulley for a round belt.

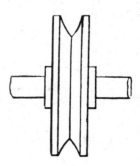

No. 4

A smooth-surface V-grooved pulley for a round belt.

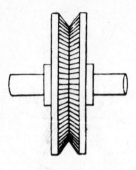

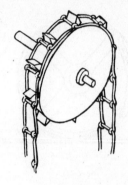

No. 5

A V-grooved pulley having its groove notched to increase the adhesion of the belt or rope.

No. 7

Another kind of chain and pulley.

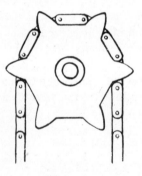

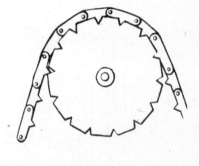

No. 6

Represents a chain and chain pulley. The links being in different planes, spaces are left between them for the teeth of the pulley to enter.

No. 8

Similar to No. 6 but differing from it in that the engaging teeth are on the chain rather than on the pulley.

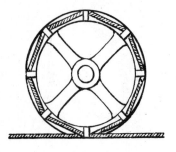

No. 9

Uniform circular motion into rectilinear by means of a rope or band, which is wound one or more times around the drum.

No. 11

This represents an expanding pulley. On turning pinion, *d*, to the right or left, a similar motion is imparted to wheel, *c*, which, by means of curved slots cut therein, thrusts the studs fastened to arms of pulley outward or inward, thus augmenting or diminishing the size of the pulley.

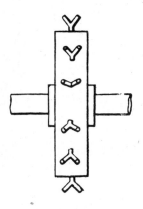

No. 10

A sprocket-wheel to drive or to be driven by a chain or rope.

No. 12

Illustrates the transmission of power by simple pulleys and an open belt. In this case both of the pulleys rotate in the same direction.

driven, the middle one fast and the other two loose upon it, and using both an open and a crossed belt, the direction of the said shaft is enabled to be reversed without stopping or reversing the driver. One belt will always run on the fast pulley, and the other on one of the loose pulleys. The shaft will be driven in one direction or the other, according as the open or crossed belt is on the fast pulley.

No. 13

Differs from No. 12 in the substitution of a crossed belt for the open one. In this case the direction of rotation of the pulleys is reversed.

By arranging three pulleys, side by side, upon the shaft to be

No. 14

Resembles No. 13, with the addition of a movable tightening pulley, B. When this pulley is pressed against the band to take up the slack, the belt transmits motion from one of the larger pulleys to the other; but when it is not, the belt is so slack as not to transmit motion.

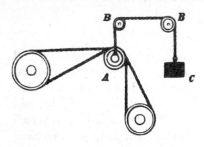

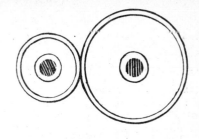

No. 16

No. 15

A contrivance for transmitting rotary motion to a movable pulley. The pulley at the bottom of the figure is the movable one; if this pulley were raised or depressed, the belt would be slackened or tightened accordingly. In order to keep a uniform tension on the belt, a pulley, A, carried in a frame sliding between guides (not shown), hangs from a rope passing over the two guide-pulleys, B, B, and is acted upon by the balance weight, C, in such manner as to produce the desired result. If a round belt is used, wrapping it an extra turn around driver pulley will add driving power to the belt, and will eliminate use of belt tightener as shown in No. 14.

The weight, C, and the guide pulleys, B, B, may of course be replaced by a spring.

Friction-wheels. The surfaces of these wheels are made rough so as to bite as much as possible; one is sometimes faced with leather, or, better, with vulcanized india-rubber. Relative speeds depend on diameter of driver and driven discs.

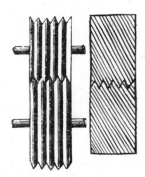

No. 17

These "V" grooved friction drives are for heavy duty as the friction surface is doubled over that of flat belt contact in same width.

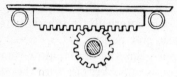

No. 18

Circular into rectilinear motion, or *vice versa*, by means of rack and pinion.

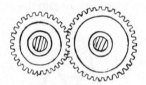

No. 19

Spur gear. All meshing teeth are same shape and relative speed ratios are determined by number of teeth in driver and driven.

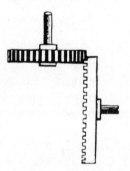

No. 20

The wheel to the right is termed a "crown-wheel"; that gearing with it is a spur-gear.

These wheels are not much used, and are only available for light work, as the teeth of the crown-wheel must necessarily be thin.

No. 21

Bevel-gears. Those of equal diameters are termed "miter-gears."

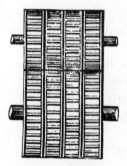

No. 22

A kind of gearing used to transmit great force and give a continuous bearing to the teeth. Each wheel is composed of two, three, or more distinct spur-gears. The teeth, instead of being in line, are arranged in steps to give a continuous bearing. This system is sometimes used for driving screw propellers, and sometimes, with a rack of similar character, to drive the beds of large iron-planing machines.

No. 23

Rotary converted into rotary motion. The teeth of these gears, being oblique, give a more continuous bearing than ordinary spur-gears. These diagonal cut gears are nearly silent in operation.

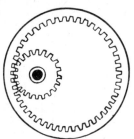

No. 24

An internally toothed spur-gear and pinion. With ordinary spur-gears the direction of rotation is opposite; but with the internally toothed gear, the two rotate in the same direction; and with the same strength of tooth the gears are capable of transmitting greater force, because more teeth are engaged.

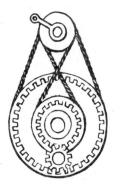

No. 25

The small pulley at the top being the driver, the large, internally-toothed gear and the concentric gear within will be driven in opposite directions by the bands, and at the same time will impart motion to the intermediate pinion at the bottom, both around its own center and also around the common center of the two concentric gears.

3. BEARINGS

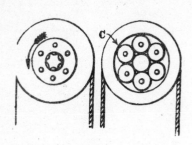

No. 26

This is what is known as a roller-bearing. Cylinders, C, intervene between the inner surface of the pulley and the shaft.

No. 27

Anti-friction bearing. Instead of a shaft revolving in an ordinary bearing it is sometimes supported on the circumference of wheels. The friction is thus reduced to the least amount.

II.

The Control of Simple Mechanical Movement

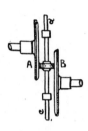

No. 28

Friction gear. A pair of friction discs A, B, on parallel shafts out of line, with a traverse friction pinion on a transverse spindle *c, d* will give a great range of speed velocities.

per wheel, A, shown in section, is composed of a rubber disc with V-edge, clamped between two metal plates. By screwing up the nut, B, which holds the parts together, the rubber disc is made to expand radially, and greater tractive power may be produced between the two wheels.

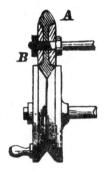

No. 29

J. W. Howlett's patent adjustable frictional gearing. The up-

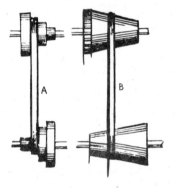

No. 30

a. Variable speed-pulleys used for lathes and other mechanical tools, for varying the speed according to the work operated upon.

b. Cone-pulleys for the same purpose as a. This motion is

used in cotton machinery, and in all machines which are required to run with a gradually increased or diminished speed. (Belt shift must, of course, be used to move belt to position of required speed and to hold it there.)

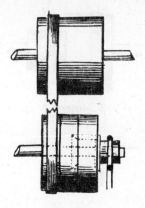

No. 32

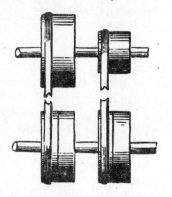

No. 31

For transmitting two speeds by means of belts. There are four pulleys on the lower shaft, the two outer ones being loose and the two inner ones fast. The band to the left is shown on its loose pulley, the one to the right on its fast one; a slow motion is consequently transmitted to lower shaft. When band to the right is moved on to its loose pulley, and left-hand one on to its fast pulley, a quicker motion is transmitted.

For transmitting two speeds, one a differential motion. The band is shown on a loose pulley on lower shaft. The middle pulley is fast on said shaft, and has a small bevel-gear secured to its hub. Pulley on the right, which, like that on the left, is loose on shaft, carries, transversely, another bevel-gear. A third bevel-gear, loose upon the shaft, is held by a friction-band which is weighted at the end. On moving belt on middle pulley a simple motion is the result, but when it is moved to right-hand pulley a double speed is given to shaft. The friction-belt or curb on the third bevel-gear is to allow it to slip a little on a sudden change of speed.

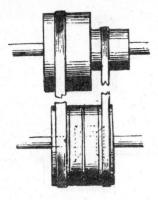

No. 33

For transmitting two speeds, one of which is a different and variable motion. This is very similar to the last, except in the third bevel-gear being attached to a fourth pulley, at the right of the other three, and driven by a belt from a small pulley on shaft above. When left-hand belt is on the pulley carrying the middle bevel-gear, and pulley at the right turns in the same direction, the amount of rotation of the third bevel-gear must be deducted from the double speed which the shaft would have if this gear was at rest. If, on the contrary, the right-hand belt be crossed so as to turn the pulley in an opposite direction, that amount must be added.

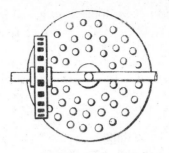

No. 34

A pin-wheel and slotted pinion, by which three changes of speed can be obtained. There are three circles of pins of equal distance on the face of the pinwheel, and by shifting the slotted pinion along its shaft, to bring it in contact with one or the other of the circles of pins, a continuous rotary motion of the wheel is made to produce three changes of speed of the pinion, or *vice versa*.

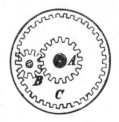

No. 35

Different velocity given to two gears, A and C, on the same shaft, by the pinion, B.

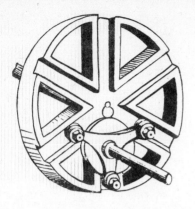

No. 36

Multiple gearing. The smaller triangular wheel drives the larger one by the movement of its attached friction-rollers in the radial grooves.

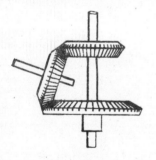

No. 37

A mode of obtaining two different speeds on the same shaft from one driving-wheel. One of the bevel-gears to be mounted on sleeve on drive shaft.

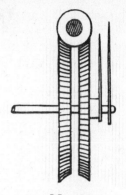

No. 38

Two worm-wheels of equal diameter, but one having one tooth more than the other, both in gear with the same worm. Suppose the first wheel has 100 teeth and the second 101, one wheel will gain one revolution over the other during the passage of 100×101 teeth of either wheel across the plane of centers, or during 10,100 revolutions of the worm.

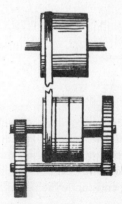

No. 39

For transmitting two speeds by gearing. The band is shown on the loose pulley—the left-hand one of the lower three. The middle pulley is fixed on the same shaft as the small pinion, and the pulley to the right on a hollow shaft, on the end of which is fixed the large spur-gear. When the band is on the middle pulley a slow motion is transmitted to the shaft below; but when it is on the right-hand pulley a quick speed is given, proportionate to the diameter of the gears.

small spur-gear. The next pulley is fixed on a hollow shaft running on the main shaft, and there is secured to it a second spur-gear, larger than the first. The fourth and last pulley to the left is fixed on another hollow shaft running loosely on the last-named, on the other end of which is fixed the still larger spur-gear nearest to the pulley. As the band is made to traverse from one pulley to another, it transmits three different velocities to the shaft below.

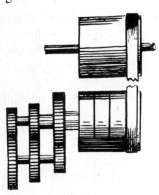

No. 40

For transmitting three different speeds by gearing. The lower part of the band is shown on a loose pulley. The next pulley is fixed on the main shaft, on the other end of which is fixed a

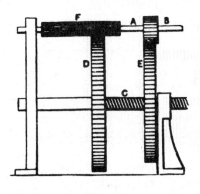

No. 41

A differential movement. The screw, C, works in a nut secured to the hub of the wheel, E, the nut being free to turn in a bearing in the shorter standard, but prevented by the bearing from any lateral motion. The screw-shaft is secured in the wheel, D. The driving-shaft, A, carries two pinions, F and B. If these pinions were of such size as to turn the two wheels, D and E, with an equal velocity, the screw would remain at rest; but the said wheels being driven at unequal velocities, the screw travels according to the difference of velocity.

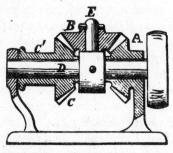

No. 42

Entwistle's patent gearing. Bevel-gear, A, is fixed. B, gearing with A, is fitted to rotate on stud, E, secured to shaft, D, and it also gears with bevel-gear, C, loose, on the shaft, D. On rotary motion being given to shaft, D, the gear, E, revolves around A, and also rotates upon its own axis, and so acts upon C in two ways, namely, by its rotation on its own axis and by its revolution around A. With three gears of equal size, the gear, C, makes two revolutions for every one of the

shaft, D. This velocity of revolution may, however, be varied by changing the relative sizes of the gears. C is represented with an attached drum, C'. This gearing may be used for steering apparatus, driving screw-propellers, etc. By applying power to C, action may be reversed, and a slow motion of D obtained.

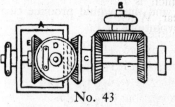

No. 43

This movement is designed to double the speed by gears of equal diameters and numbers of teeth—a result once generally supposed to be impossible. Six bevel-gears are employed. The gear on the shaft, B, is in gear with two others—one on the shaft, F, and the other on the same hollow shaft with C, which turns loosely on F. The gear, D, is carried by the frame, A, which, being fast on the shaft, F, is made to rotate, and therefore takes round D with it. E is loose on the shaft, F, and gears with D. Now, suppose the two gears on the hollow shaft, C, were removed and D prevented from turning on its axis; one revolution given to the gear on B would cause the frame, A, also to receive one revolution, and as this frame carries with it the gear, D, gearing with E, one revolution would be imparted to E; but if the gears on the hollow shaft, C, were replaced, D would receive also a revolution on its axis during the one revolution of B, and thus would produce two revolutions of E.

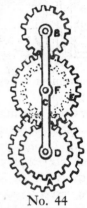

No. 44

An "epicyclic train." Any train of gearing, the axes of the wheels of which revolve around a common center, is properly known by this name. The wheel at one end of such a train, if not those at both ends, is always concentric with the revolving frame. C is the frame or train-bearing arm. The center wheel, A, concentric with this frame, gears with a pinion, F, to the same axle with which is secured a wheel, F, that gears with a wheel, B. If the first wheel, A, be fixed and a motion be given to the frame, C, the train will revolve around the fixed wheel and the relative motion of the frame to the fixed wheel will communicate through the train a rotary motion to B on its axis. Or the first wheel as well as the frame may be made to revolve with different velocities, with the same result except as to the velocity of rotation of B upon its axis.

In the epicyclic train as thus described only the wheel at one extremity is concentric with the revolving frame; but if the wheel, E, instead of gearing with B, be made to gear with the wheel, D, which like the wheel, A, is concentric with the frame, we have an epicyclic train of which the wheels at both extremities are concentric with the frame. In this train we may either communicate the driving motion to the arm and one extreme wheel, in order to produce an aggregate rotation of the other extreme wheel, or motion may be given to the two extreme wheels, A and D, of the train, and the aggregate motion will thus be communicated to the arm.

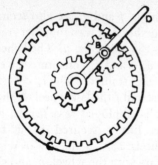

No. 45

Another simple form of the epicyclic train, in which the arm, D, carries a pinion, B, which gears both with a spur-wheel, A, and an annular wheel, C, both concentric with the axis of the arm. Either of the wheels, A, C, may be stationary, and the revolution of the arm and pinion will give motion to the other wheel.

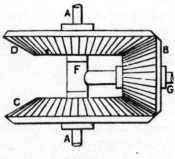

No. 46

A very simple form of the epicyclic train, in which F, G, is the arm, secured to the central shaft, A, upon which are

loosely fitted the bevel-wheels, C, D. The arm is formed into an axle for the bevel-wheel, B, which is fitted to turn freely upon it. Motion may be given to the two wheels, C, D, in order to produce aggregate motion of the arm, or else to the arm and one of said wheels in order to produce aggregate motion of the other wheel.

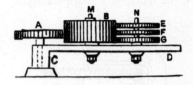

No. 47

Ferguson's mechanical paradox, designed to show a curious property of the epicyclic train. The wheel, A, is fixed upon a stationary stud about which the arm, C, D, revolves. In this arm are two pins, M, N, upon one of which is fitted loosely a thick wheel, B, gearing with A, and upon the other are three loose wheels, E, F, G, all gearing with B. When the arm, C, D, is turned round on the stud, motion is given to the three wheels, E, F, G, on their common axis, viz., the pin, N; the three forming with the intermediate wheel,

B, and the wheel, A, three distinct epicyclic trains. Suppose A to have twenty teeth, F twenty, E twenty-one, and G nineteen; as the arm, E, C, D, is turned round, F will appear not to turn on its axis, as any point in its circumference will always point in one direction, while E will appear to turn slowly in one and G in the other direction, which—an apparent paradox—gave rise to the name of the apparatus.

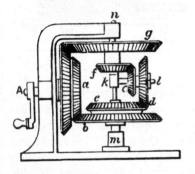

No. 48

Another epicyclic train in which neither the first nor last wheel is fixed. *m, n,* is a shaft to which is firmly secured the train-bearing arm, *k, l,* which carries the two wheels, *d, e,* secured together, but rotating upon the arm itself. The wheels, *b* and *c,* are united and turn together, freely upon the shaft. *m, n;* the

wheels, *f* and *g,* are also secured together, but turn together freely on the shaft, *m, n.* The wheels, *c, d, e* and *f,* constitute an epicyclic train of which *c* is the first and *f* the last wheel. A shaft, A, is employed as a driver, and has firmly secured to it two wheels, *a* and *h,* the first of which gears with the wheel, *b,* and thus communicates motion to the first wheel, *c,* of the epicyclic train, and the wheel, *h,* drives the wheel, *g,* which thus gives motion to the last wheel, *f.* Motion communicated in this way to the two ends of the train produces an aggregate motion of the arm, *k, l,* and shaft, *m, n.*

This train may be modified; for instance, suppose the wheels, *g* and *f,* to be disunited, *g* to be fixed to the shaft, *m, n,* and *f* only running loose upon it. The driving-shaft, A, will as before communicate motion to the first wheel, *c,* of the epicyclic train by means of the wheels, *a* and *b,* and will also by *h* cause the wheel, *g,* the shaft, *m, n,* and the train-bearing arm, *k, l,* to revolve, and the aggregate rotation will be given to the loose wheel, *f.*

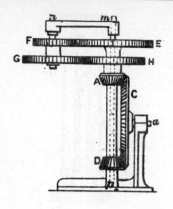

No. 49

No. 50

Another form of epicyclic train designed for producing a very slow motion. *m* is a fixed shaft upon which is loosely fitted a long sleeve, to the lower end of which is fixed a wheel, D, and to the upper end a wheel, E. Upon this long sleeve there is fitted a shorter one which carries at its extremities the wheels A and H. A wheel, C, gears with both D and A, and a train-bearing arm, *m*, *n*, which revolves freely upon the shaft, *m*, *p*, carries upon a stud at *n* the united wheels, F and G. If A has 10 teeth, C 100, D 10, E 61, F 49, G 41, and H 51, there will be 25,000 revolutions of the train-bearing arm, *m*, *n*, for one of the wheel, C.

a. Simple pulley used for lifting weights. In this the power must be equal to the weight to obtain equilibrium.

b. In this the lower pulley is movable. One end of the rope being fixed, the other must move twice as fast as the weight, and a corresponding gain of power is consequently effected.

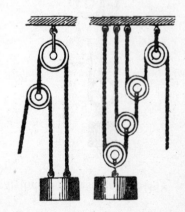

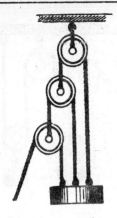 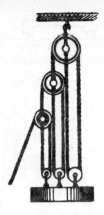

No. 51

The following rule applies to these pulleys:—In a system of pulleys where each pulley is embraced by a cord attached at one end to a fixed point and at the other to the center of the movable pulley, the effect of the whole will be = the number 2, multiplied by itself as many times as there are movable pulleys in the system.

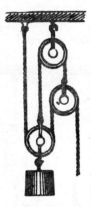 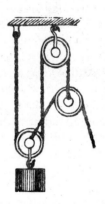

No. 52

These combinations of pulleys are known as Spanish bartons.

No. 53

A combination of two fixed pulleys and one movable pulley.

No. 55

Represents what are known as White's pulleys, which can either be made with separate loose pulleys, or a series of grooves can be cut in a solid block, the diameters being made in proportion to the speed of the rope; that is, 1, 3, and 5 for one block, and 2, 4, and 6 for the other. Power as 1 to 7.

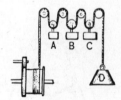

No. 54

Blocks and tackle. The power obtained by this contrivance is calculated as follows: Divide the weight by double the number of pulleys in the lower block; the quotient is the power required to balance the weight.

No. 56

Compound weight motor, for a limited fall. The power is only equal to one-half of one of the weights. The time of falling and distance equals three times the time and distance of one weight.

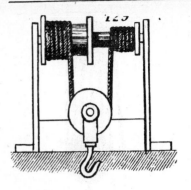

No. 57

Chinese windlass. This embraces the same principles as the micrometer screw. The movement of the pulley in every revolution of the windlass is equal to half the difference between the larger and smaller circumferences of the windlass barrel.

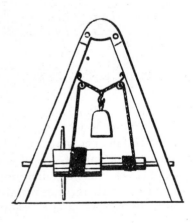

No. 58

Another arrangement of the Chinese windlass illustrated in this table.

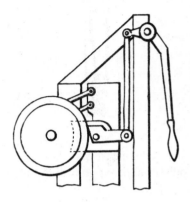

No. 59

A mode of working a windlass. By the alternating motion of the long hand-lever to the right, motion is communicated to the short lever, the end of which is in immediate contact with the rim of the wheel. The short lever has a very limited motion upon a pin, which is fixed in a block of cast-iron, which is made with two jaws, each having a flange projecting inward in contact with the inner surface of the rim of the wheel. By the upward motion of the outward end of the short lever, the rim of the wheel is jammed between the end of the lever and the flanges of the block, so as to cause friction sufficient to turn the wheel by the further upward movement of the lever. The backward movement of the wheel is prevented by a common ratchet-wheel and pawls; as the short lever is pushed down it frees the wheel and slides freely over it.

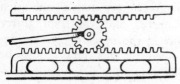

No. 60

A mode of doubling the length of stroke of a piston-rod, or the throw of a crank. A pinion revolving on a spindle attached to the connecting-rod or pitman is in gear with a fixed rack. Another rack carried by a guide-rod above, and in gear with the opposite side of the pinion, is free to traverse backward and forward. Now, as the connecting-rod communicates to the pinion the full length of stroke, it would cause the top rack to traverse the same distance, if the bottom rack was alike movable; but as the latter is fixed, the pinion is made to rotate, and consequently the top rack travels double the distance.

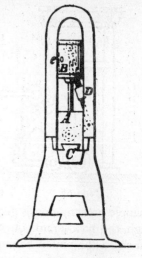

No. 61

Hotchkiss's atmospheric hammer; derives the force of its blow from compressed air. Hammer head, C, is attached to a piston fitted to a cylinder, B, which is connected by a rod, D, with a crank, A, on the rotary driving-shaft. As the cylinder ascends, air entering hole, e, is compressed below piston and lifts hammer. As cylinder descends, air entering hole, e, is compressed above and is stored up to produce the blow by its instant expansion after the crank and connecting-rod turn bottom center.

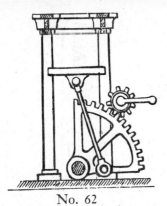

No. 62

A simple press motion is given through the hand-crank on the pinion-shaft; the pinion communicating motion to the toothed sector, which acts upon the platen, by means of the rod which connects it therewith. The combination of leverages through hand crank, pinion, sector and placement of fulcrum on pitman-rod end provides a powerful pressure.

No. 63

Hydrostatic press. Water forced by the pump through the small pipe into the ram cylinder and under the solid ram, presses up the ram. The amount of force obtained is in proportion to the relative areas or squares of diameters of the pump-plunger and ram. Suppose, for instance, the pump-plunger to be one inch diameter and the ram thirty inches, the upward pressure received by the ram would be 900 times the downward pressure of the plunger.

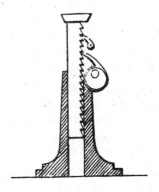

No. 64

Lifting-jack operated by an eccentric, pawl, and ratchet. The upper pawl is a stop.

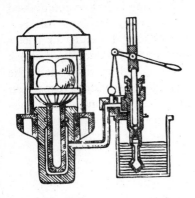

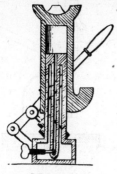

No. 65

Robertson's hydrostatic jack. In this the ram is stationary upon a hollow base and the cylinder with claw attached slides upon it. The pump takes the water from the hollow base and forces it through a pipe in the ram into the cylinder, and so raises the latter. At the bottom of pipe there is a valve operated by a thumb-screw to let back the water and lower the load as gradually as may be desired.

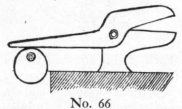

No. 66

Shears for cutting iron plates, etc. The jaws are opened by the weight of the long arm of the upper one, and closed by the rotation of the cam.

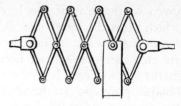

No. 67

A system of crossed levers, termed "Lazy Tongs." A short alternating rectilinear motion of rod at the right will give a similar but much greater motion to rod at the left. It is frequently used in children's toys. It has been applied in France to a machine for raising sunken vessels; also applied to ships' pumps, three-quarters of a century ago.

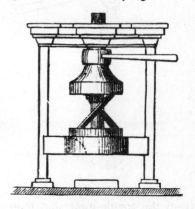

No. 68

This is a motion which has been used in presses to produce the necessary pressure upon the platen. Horizontal motion is given to the arm of the lever which turns the upper disc. Between the top and bottom discs are two bars which enter holes in the discs. These bars are in oblique positions, as shown in the drawing, when the press is not in operation; but when the top disc is made to rotate, the bars move toward perpendicular positions and force the lower disc down. The top disc must be firmly secured in a stationary position, except as to its revolution.

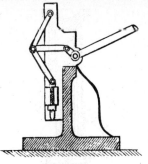

No. 70

The toggle-joint arranged for a punching machine. Lever at the right is made to operate upon the joint of the toggle by means of the horizontal connecting-link.

No. 69

A knee-lever, differing slightly from the toggle-joint shown in 40. It is often used for presses and stamps, as a great force can be obtained by it. The action is by raising or lowering the horizontal lever.

No. 71

Each jaw is attached to one of the two segments, one of which has teeth outside and the other teeth inside. On turning the shaft carrying the two pinions, one of which gears with one and the other with the other segment, the jaws are brought together with great force.

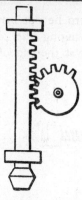

No. 72

Stamp. Vertical percussive falls derived from horizontal rotating shaft. The mutilated toothed pinion acts upon the rack to raise the rod until its teeth leave the rack and allow the rod to fall.

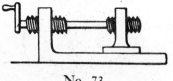

No. 73

The shaft has two screws of different pitches cut on it, one screwing into a fixed bearing, and the other into a bearing free to move to and fro. Rotary motion of the shaft gives rectilinear motion to the movable bearing, a distance equal to the difference of pitches, at each revolution.

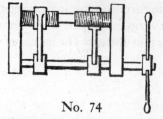

No. 74

Uniform circular into uniform rectilinear motion; used in spooling-frames for leading or guiding the thread on to the spools. The roller is divided into two parts, each having a fine screw thread cut upon it, one a right and the other a left hand screw. The spindle parallel with the roller has arms which carry two half-nuts, fitted to the screws, one over and the other under the roller. When one half-nut is in, the other is out of gear. By pressing the lever to the right or left, the rod is made to traverse in either direction.

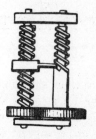

No. 75

The rotation of the screw at the left hand side produces a

uniform rectilinear movement of a cutter which cuts another screw thread. The pitch of the screw to be cut may be varied by changing the sizes of the wheels at the end of the frame.

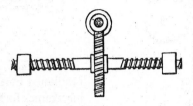

No. 76

Continuous circular into continuous but much slower rectilinear motion. The worm on the upper shaft, acting on the toothed wheel on the screw-shaft, causes the right and left hand screw-threads to move the nuts upon them toward or from each other according to the direction of rotation.

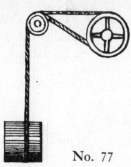

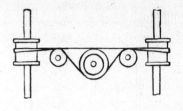

No. 79

Represents a mode of transmitting power from a horizontal shaft to two vertical ones by means of pulleys and a band.

No. 77

A method of transmitting motion from a shaft at right angles to another, by means of guide-pulleys. There are two of these pulleys, side by side, one for each leaf of the belt.

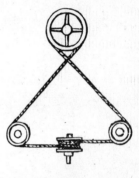

No. 80

A method of transmitting motion from a shaft at right angles to another whose axis is in the same plane. This is shown with a crossed belt. An open belt may be used, but the crossed one is preferable, as it gives more surface of contact. In substitution

No. 78

Another method of effecting the same results as 77, without guide-pulleys. Face of driven pulley must be directly under spot where belt center leaves driver pulley.

of crossed belt for straight belt, the rotation of driven pulley is reversed.

No. 81

A movement used in transferring power from a vertical shaft to a shaft at an angle to it.

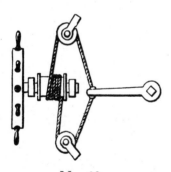

No. 82

Ordinary steering apparatus. Plan view. On the shaft of the hand-wheel there is a barrel on which is wound a rope which passes round the guide-pulleys and has its opposite ends attached to the "tiller" or lever on the top of the rudder; by turning the wheel, one end of the rope is wound on and the other let off, and the tiller is moved in one or the other direction, according to the direction in which the wheel is turned.

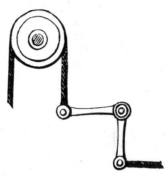

No. 83

A bell-crank lever, used for changing the direction of any force.

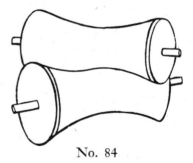

No. 84

An illustration of the transmission of rotary motion from one shaft to another, arranged obliquely to it, by means of rolling contact.

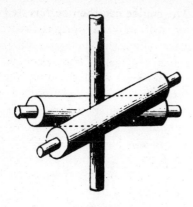

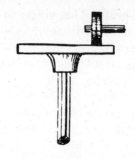

No. 87

These are sometimes called "brush-wheels." The relative speeds can be varied by changing the distance of the upper wheel from the center of the lower one. The one drives the other by the friction or adhesion, and this may be increased by facing the lower one with india-rubber.

No. 85

Cylindrical rod arranged between two rollers, the axes of which are oblique to each other. The rotation of the rollers produces both a longitudinal and a rotary motion of the rod.

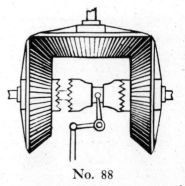

No. 86

Different kinds of gears for transmitting rotary motion from one shaft to another arranged obliquely thereto.

No. 88

The vertical shaft is made to drive the horizontal one in either direction, as may be desired, by means of the double-clutch and bevel-gears. The gears on the horizontal shaft are loose, and are driven in opposite directions by the third gear; the double-clutch slides upon a key or feather fixed on the horizontal shaft, which is made to rotate either to the right or left, according to the side on which it is engaged.

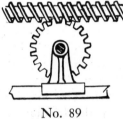

No. 89

In this, rotary motion is imparted to the wheel by the rotation of the screw, or rectilinear motion of the slide by the rotation of the wheel. Used in screw-cutting and slide-lathes.

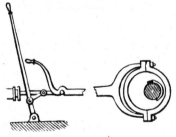

No. 90

Reversing-gear for a single engine. On raising the eccentric-rod the valve-spindle is released.

The engine can then be reversed by working the upright lever, after which the eccentric-rod is let down again. The eccentric in this case is loose upon the shaft and driven by a projection on the shaft acting upon a nearly semi-circular projection on the side of the eccentric, which permits the eccentric to turn halfway round on the shaft on reversing the valves.

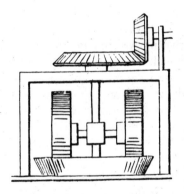

No. 91

Pair of edge runners or chasers for crushing or grinding. The axles are connected with vertical shaft, and the wheels or chasers run in an annular pan or trough.

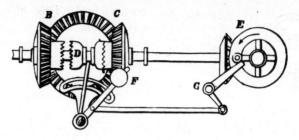

No. 92

A contrivance for a self-reversing motion. The bevel-gear between the gears, B and C, is the driver. The gears, B and C, run loose upon the shaft, consequently motion is only communicated when one or other of them is engaged with the clutch, D, which slides on a feather on the shaft and is shown in gear with C. The wheel, E, at the right, is driven by bevel-gearing from the shaft on which the gears, B, C, and clutch are placed, and is about to strike the bell-crank, G, and produce such a movement thereof as will cause the connecting-rod to carry the weighted lever, F, beyond a perpendicular position, when the said lever will fall over suddenly to the left, and carry the clutch into gear with B, thereby reversing the motion of the shaft, until the stud in the wheel, E, coming round in the contrary direction, brings the weighted lever back past the perpendicular position, and thereby again causes it to reverse the motion.

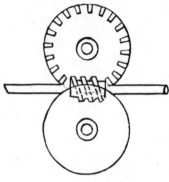

No. 93

A mode of driving a pair of feed-rolls, the opposite surfaces of which require to move in the same direction. The two wheels are precisely similar, and both gear into the endless screw which is arranged between them. The teeth of one wheel only are visible, those of the other being on the back or side which is concealed from view.

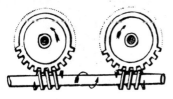

No. 94

A modification of 93 by means of two worms and worm-wheels.

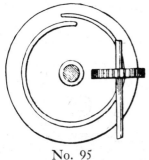

No. 95

Transmission of rotary motion from one shaft at right angles to another. The spiral thread of the disc-wheel drives the spur-gear, moving it the distance of one tooth at every revolution.

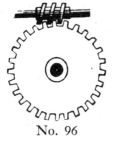

No. 96

Worm or endless screw and a

worm-wheel. This effects the same result as 95; and as it is more easily constructed, it is oftener used.

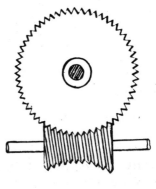

No. 97

Worm or endless screw and worm-wheel. Used when steadiness or great power is required.

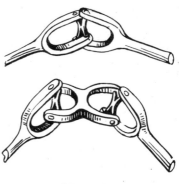

No. 98

Two kinds of universal joints.

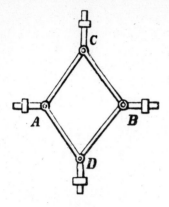

No. 100

No. 99

Rectilinear into rectilinear motion. When the rods, A and B, are brought together, the rods, C and D, are thrust further apart, and *vice versa*.

A nearly continuous rotary motion is given to the wheel, D, by two ratchet-toothed arcs, C, one operating on each side of the ratchet-wheel, D. These arcs (only one of which is shown) are fast on the same rock-shaft, B, and have their teeth set opposite ways. The rock-shaft is worked by giving a reciprocating rectilinear motion to the rod, A. The arcs should have springs applied to them, so that each may be capable of rising to allow its teeth to slide over those of the wheel in moving one way.

III.

Timing and Regulation of Movement

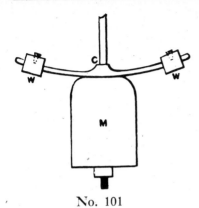

No. 101

Compound bar compensation pendulum. C is a compound bar of brass and iron or steel, brazed together with brass downward. As brass expands more than iron, the bar will bend upward as it gets warmer, and carry the weights, W, W, up with it, raising the center of the aggregate weight, M, W, to raise the center of oscillation as much as elongation of the pendulum-rod would let it down.

No. 102

Conical pendulum, hung by a thin piece of round wire. Lower end connected with and driven in a circle by an arm attached to a vertical rotating spindle. The pendulum-rod describes a cone in its revolution.

No. 103

Mercurial compensation pendulum. A glass jar of mercury is used for the bob or weight. As the pendulum-rod is expanded lengthwise by increased temperature, the expansion of mercury in jar carries it to a greater height therein, and so raises its center of gravity relatively to the rod sufficiently to compensate for downward expansion of the rod. As rod is contracted by a reduction of temperature, contraction of mercury lowers it relatively to rod. In this way the center of oscillation is always kept in the same place, and the effective length of pendulum always the same.

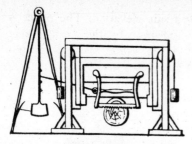

No. 104

Saw for cutting trees by motion of pendulum is represented as cutting a lying tree.

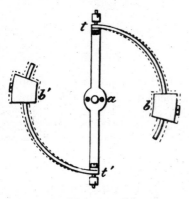

No. 105

Compensation balance. t, a, t', is the main bar of balance, with timing screws for regulation at the ends. t and t' are two compound bars, of which the outside is brass and the inside steel, carrying weights, b, b'. As heat increases, these bars are bent inward by the greater expansion of the brass, and the weights are thus drawn inward, diminishing

the inertia of the balance. As the heat diminishes, an opposite effect is produced. This balance compensates both for its own expansion and contraction, and that of the balance-spring.

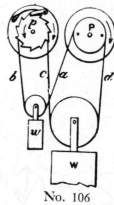

No. 106

Endless chain, maintaining power on going-barrel, to keep a clock going while winding, during which operation the action of the weight or main-spring is taken off the barrel. The wheel to the right is the "going-wheel," and that to the left the "striking-wheel." P is a pulley fixed to the great wheel of the going part, and roughened, to prevent a rope or chain hung over it from slipping. A similar pulley rides on another arbor, p, which may be the arbor of the great wheel of the striking part, and attached by a ratchet and click to that wheel, or to clock-frame, if there is no striking part. The weights are hung, as may be seen, the small one being only large enough to keep the rope or chain on the pulleys. If the part, *b*, of the rope or chain is pulled down, the ratchet-pulley runs under the click, and the great weight is pulled up by *c*, without taking its pressure off the going-wheel at all.

b a side elevation. The pallet is acted upon by the teeth of one and the other of two escape-wheels alternately.

No. 108

Another kind of pendulum escapement. This is the escapement first used in wooden clock construction.

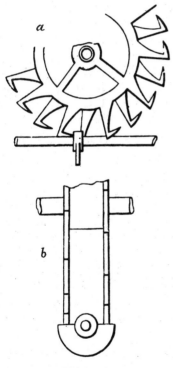

No. 107

A clock or watch escapement; *a* being a front elevation, and

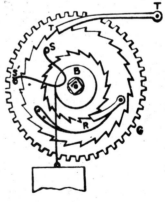

No. 109

Harrison's "going-barrel." Larger ratchet-wheel, to which

the click, R, is attached, is connected with the great wheel, G, by a spring, S, S'. While the clock is going, the weight acts upon the great wheel, G, through the spring; but as soon as the weight is taken off by winding, the click, T, whose pivot is set in the frame, prevents the larger ratchet from falling back, and so the spring, S, S', still drives the great wheel during the time the clock takes to wind, as it need only just keep the escapement going, the pendulum taking care of itself for that short time. Good watches have a substantially similar apparatus.

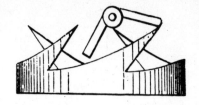

No. 111

An old-fashioned clock escapement.

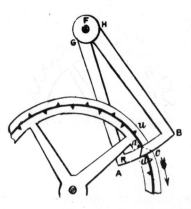

No. 112

Stud escapement, used in large clocks. One pallet, B, works in front of the wheel and the other at the back. The studs are arranged in the same manner, and rest alternately upon the front or back pallet. As the curve of the pallets is an arc described from F, this is a *repose* or *dead-beat* escapement.

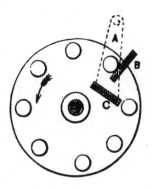

No. 110

An escapement with a lantern wheel. An arm, A, carries the two pallets, B and C.

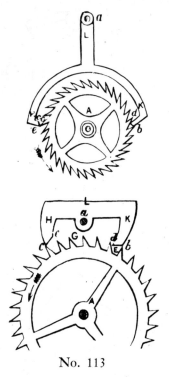

No. 113

the lower these surfaces are cut to a curve concentric to the axis, *a;* consequently, during the time one of the teeth is against the pallet the wheel remains perfectly at rest. Hence the name *repose* or *dead-beat*. In the upper the surfaces are of a different form, not necessary to explain, as it can be understood that any form not concentric with the axis, *a*, must produce a slight recoil of the wheel during the escape of the tooth, and hence the term *recoil* escapement. On the pallets leaving teeth, at each oscillation of the pendulum, the extremities of teeth slide along the surfaces, *c, e,* and *d, b,* and give sufficient impulse to pendulum.

The upper is what is termed a *recoil*, and the lower a *repose* or *dead-beat* escapement for clocks. The same letters of reference indicate like parts in both. The *anchor*, H, L, K, is caused, by the oscillation of the pendulum, to vibrate upon the axis, *a*. Between the two extremities, or pallets, H, K, is placed the escape-wheel, A, the teeth of which come alternately against the outer surface of the pallet, K, and inner surface of pallet, H. In

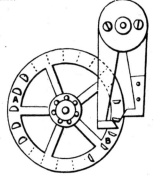

No. 114

Pin-wheel escapement, somewhat resembling the stud escapement shown by 111. The pins, A, B, of the escape-wheel are of two different forms, but the form of those on the right side is the best. One advantage of this kind of escapement is that if one of the pins is damaged it can easily be replaced, whereas if a tooth is damaged the whole wheel is ruined.

No. 115

Lever escapement. The anchor or piece, B, which carries the pallets, is attached to lever, E, C, at one end of which is a notch, E. On a disc secured on the arbor of balance is fixed a small pin which enters the notch at the middle of each vibration, causing the pallet to enter in and retire from between the teeth of escape-wheel. The wheel gives an impulse to each of the pallets alternately as it leaves a tooth, and the lever gives impulse to the balance-wheel in opposite directions alternately.

No. 116

Lever chronometer escapement. In this the pallets, A, B, and lever, look like those of the lever escapement 117: but these pallets only lock the escape-wheel, having no impulse. Impulse is given by teeth of escape-wheel directly to a pallet, C, attached to balance.

No. 117

Mudge's gravity escapement. The pallets, A, B, instead of being on one arbor, are on two, as shown at C. The pendulum plays between the fork-pins, P, Q, and so raises one of the weighted pallets out of the wheel at each vibration. When the pendulum returns the pallet falls with it, and the weight of the pallet gives the impulse.

formed in an opening in a plate attached to the pendulum, and the three teeth of the escape-wheel operate on the upper and lower pallets alternately. One tooth is shown in operation on the upper pallet.

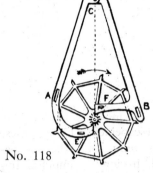

No. 118

Bloxam's gravity escapement. The pallets are lifted alternately by the small wheel, and the stopping is done by the action of the stops, A and B, on the larger wheel. E and F are the fork-pins which embrace the pendulum.

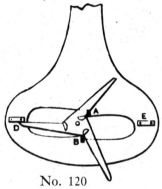

No. 120

A modification of 117 with long stopping teeth, D and E. A and B are the pallets.

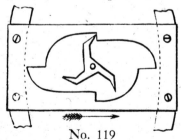

No. 119

Three-legged pendulum escapement. The pallets are

No. 121

A single-pin pendulum escapement. The escape-wheel is a very small disc with single eccentric pin; it makes half a revolution for every beat of the pendulum, giving the impulse on the upright faces of the pallets, the horizontal faces of which are dead ones. This can also be adapted to watches.

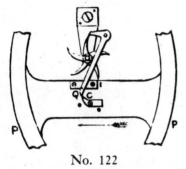

No. 122

A detached pendulum escapement, leaving the pendulum, P, free or detached from the escape-wheel, except at the time of receiving the impulse and unlocking the wheel. There is but one pallet, I, which receives impulse only during the vibrations of the pendulum to the left. The lever, Q, locks the escape-wheel until just before the time for giving the impulse, when it is unlocked by the click, C, attached to the pendulum. As the pendulum returns to the right, the click, which oscillates on a pivot, will be pushed aside by the lever.

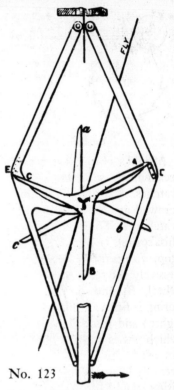

No. 123

Double three-legged gravity escapement. Two locking-wheels, A, B, C, and a, b, c, are here used with one set of lifting-pins between them. The two wheels are set wide enough apart to allow the pallets to lie between them. The teeth of the first-mentioned locking-wheel are stopped by a stop-tooth, D, on one pallet, and those of the other one by a stop-tooth, E, on the other pallet.

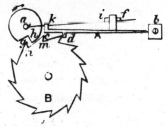

No. 124

Arnold's chronometer or free escapement, sometimes used in watches. A spring, A, is fixed or screwed against the plate of the watch at *b*. To the under side of this spring is attached a small stop, *d*, against which rest successively the teeth of the escape-wheel, B; and on the top of spring is fixed a stud, *i*, holding a lighter and more flexible spring which passes under a hook, *k*, at the extremity of A, so that it is free on being depressed, but in rising would lift A. On the axis of the balance is a small stud, *a*, which touches the thin spring at each oscillation of balance-wheel. When the movement is in the direction shown by the arrow, the stud depresses the spring in passing, but on returning raises it and the spring, A, and stop, *d*, and thus allows one tooth of escape-wheel to pass, letting them fall immediately to arrest the next. At the same time that this tooth escapes another strikes against the side of the notch, *g*, and restores to balance-wheel the force lost during a vibration. It will be understood that only at one point is the free movement of balance opposed during an oscillation.

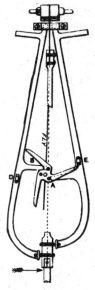

No. 125

Three-legged gravity escapement. The lifting of the pallets, A and B, is done by the three pins near the center of the escape-wheel, the pallets vibrating from two centers near the point of suspension of the pendulum. The escape-wheel is locked by means of stops, D and E, on the pallets.

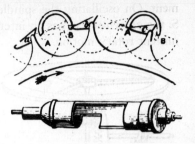

No. 128

A cylinder escapement. The cut on the left shows the cylinder in perspective, and the cut on the right shows part of the escape-wheel on a large scale, and represents the different positions taken by cylinder, A, B, during an oscillation. The pallets, *a, b, c,* on the wheel rest alternately on the inside and outside of cylinder. To the top of cylinder is attached the balance-wheel. The wheel pallets are beveled so as to keep up the impulse of balance by sliding against the beveled edge of cylinder.

No. 126

A dead-beat pendulum escapement. The inner face of the pallet, E, and outer face of D, are concentric with the axis on which the pallets vibrate, and hence there is no recoil.

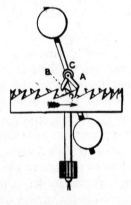

No. 127

Balance-wheel escapement. C is the balance; A, B, are the pallets; and D is the escape-wheel.

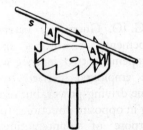

No. 129

Represents a verge escapement. On oscillating the spindle, S, the crown-wheel has an intermittent rotary motion.

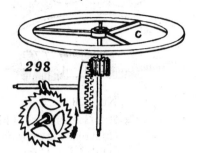

No. 130

An old-fashioned watch escapement.

No. 131

G. O. Guernsey's patent escapement for watches. In this escapement two balance-wheels are employed, carried by the same driving-power, but oscillating in opposite directions, for the purpose of counteracting the effect of any sudden jar upon a watch or time-piece. The jar

which would accelerate motion of one wheel would retard the motion of other. Anchor, A, is secured to lever, B, having an interior and exterior toothed segment at its end, each one of which gears with the pinion of balance-wheels.

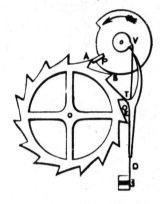

No. 132

Chronometer escapement, the form now commonly constructed. As the balance rotates in the direction of the arrow, the tooth, V, on the verge, presses the passing-spring against the lever, pressing aside the lever and removing the detent from the tooth of the escape-wheel. As balance returns, tooth, V, presses aside and passes spring without moving lever, which then rests against the stop, E. P is the only pallet upon which impulse is given.

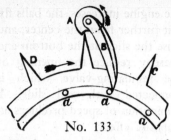

No. 133

Duplex escapement, for watches, so called from partaking of the characters of the spur and crown-wheels. The axis of balance carries pallet, B, which at every oscillation receives an impulse from the crown teeth. In the axis, A, of balance-wheel is cut a notch into which the teeth round the edge of the wheel successively fall after each one of the crown teeth passes the impulse pallet, B.

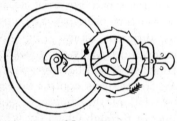

No. 134

G. P. Reed's patent anchor and lever escapement for watches. The lever is so applied in combination with chronometer escapement that the whole impulse given balance in one direction is transmitted through lever, and whole impulse in opposite direction is transmitted directly to chronometer impulse pallet, locking and unlocking the escape-wheel but once at each impulse given by said wheel.

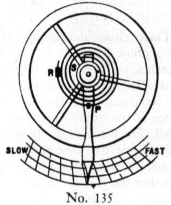

No. 135

Watch regulator. The balance-spring is attached at its outer end to a fixed stud, R, and at its inner end to staff of balance. A neutral point is formed in the spring at P by inserting it between two curb-pins in the lever, which is fitted to turn on a fixed ring concentric with staff of balance, and the spring only vibrates between this neutral point and staff of balance. By moving lever to the right, the curb-pins are made to reduce the length of acting part of spring, and the vibrations of balance are made faster; and by moving it to the left an opposite effect is produced.

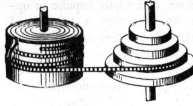

No. 136

Fusee chain and spring-box, the prime mover in some watches, particularly of English make. The fusee to the right is to compensate for the loss of force of the spring as it uncoils itself. The chain is on the small diameter of the fusee when the watch is wound up, as the spring has then the greatest force.

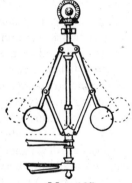

No. 137

Centrifugal governor for steam engines. The central spindle and attached arms and balls are driven from the engine by the bevel-gears at the top, and the balls fly out from the center by centrifugal force. If the speed of the engine increases, the balls fly out further from the center, and raise the slide at the bottom and thereby reduce the opening of the regulating-valve which is connected with said slide. A diminution of speed produces an opposite effect.

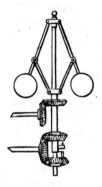

No. 138

Water-wheel governor acting on the same principle as 137, but by different means. The governor is driven by the top horizontal shaft and bevel-gears, and the lower gears control the rise and fall of the shuttle or gate over or through which the water flows to the wheel. The action is as follows:—The two bevel-gears on the lower part of the center spindle, which are furnished with studs, are fitted loosely to the said spindle and remain at rest so long as the governor has a proper velocity; but immediately that the velocity increases, the balls, flying further out, draw up the pin which is attached to a loose sleeve which slides up and down the spindle, and this pin, coming in contact with the stud on the upper bevel-gear, causes that gear to rotate with the spindle and to give motion to the lower horizontal shaft in such a direction as to make it raise the shuttle or gate, and so reduce the quantity of water passing to the wheel. On the contrary, if the speed of the governor decreases below that required, the pin falls and gives motion to the lower bevel-gear, which drives the horizontal shaft in the opposite direction and produces a contrary effect.

or gate by means of the cranked lever, which acts on the strap or belt in the following manner:— The belt runs on one of three pulleys, the middle one of which is loose on the governor spindle and the upper and lower ones fast. When the governor is running at the proper speed the belt is on the loose pulley, as shown; but when the speed increases the belt is thrown on the lower pulley, and thereby caused to act upon suitable gearing for raising the gate or shuttle and decreasing the supply of water. A reduction of the speed of the governor brings the belt on the upper pulley, which acts upon gearing for producing an opposite effect on the shuttle or gate.

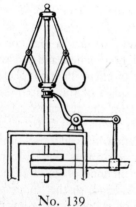

No. 139

Another arrangement for a water-wheel governor. In this the governor controls the shuttle

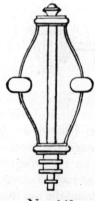

No. 140

Pickering's governor. The balls are attached to springs the

upper end of each of which is attached to a collar fixed on the spindle, and the lower end to a collar on the sliding sleeve. The springs yield in a proper degree to the centrifugal force of the balls, and raise the sleeve; and as the centrifugal force diminishes, they draw the balls toward the spindle and depress the sleeve.

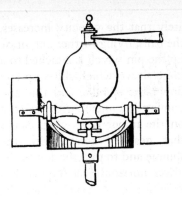

No. 142

Steam engine governor. The operation is as follows:—On engine starting the spindle revolves and carries round the cross-head to which fans are attached, and on which are also fitted two friction-rollers which bear on two circular inclined planes attached securely to the center shaft, the cross-head being loose on the shaft. The cross-head is made heavy, or has a ball or other weight attached, and is driven by the circular inclined planes. As the speed of the center shaft increases, the resistance of the air to the wings tends to retard the rotation of the cross-head; the friction-rollers therefore run up the inclined planes and raise the cross-head, to the upper part of which is connected a lever operating upon the regulating-valve of the engine.

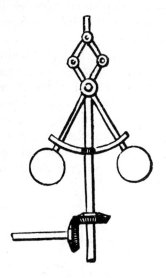

No. 141

Another form of steam engine governor. Instead of the arms being connected with a slide working on a spindle, they cross each other and are elongated upward beyond the top thereof and connected with the valve-rod by two short links.

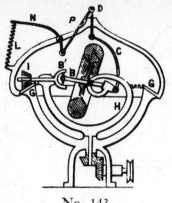

No. 143

What is called the gyroscope governor, for steam engines, etc. A is a heavy wheel, the axle, B, B^1, of which is made in two pieces connected together by a universal joint. The wheel, A, is on one piece, B, and a pinion, I, on the other piece, B^1. The piece, B, is connected at its middle by a hinge joint with the revolving frame, H, so that variations in the inclination of the wheel, A, will cause the outer end of the piece, B, to rise and fall. The frame, H, is driven by bevel gearing from the engine, and by that means the pinion, I, is carried round the stationary toothed circle, G, and the wheel, A, is thus made to receive a rapid rotary motion on its axis. When the frame, H, and wheel, A, are in motion, the tendency of the wheel, A, is to assume a vertical position, but this tendency is opposed by a spring, L. The greater the velocity of the governor, the stronger is the tendency above-mentioned, and the more it overcomes the force of the spring, and *vice versa*. The piece, B, is connected with the valve-rod by rods, C, D, and the spring, L, is connected with the said rod by levers, N, and rod, P.

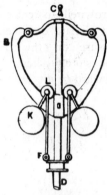

No. 144

An engine governor. The rise and fall of the balls, K, are guided by the parabolic curved arms, B, on which the antifriction wheels, L, run. The rods, F, connecting the wheels, L, with the sleeve move it up and down the spindle, C, D.

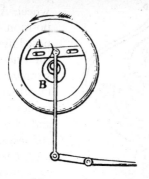

No. 145

E. P. Brownell's patent crank-motion to obviate dead-centers. The pressure on the treadle causes the slotted slide, A, to move forward with the wrist until the latter has passed the center, when the spring, B, forces the slide against the stops until it is again required to move forward.

IV.

Releases, Clamps, Brakes and Stops

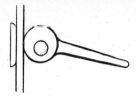

No. 146

Cam-lever grip for a rope or rod stop. This principle is used on safety grips for elevators.

No. 147

Represents varieties of stops for a ratchet-wheel.

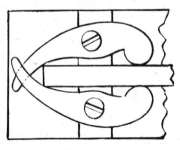

No. 148

Carpenters' bench-clamp. By pushing the clamp between the

jaws they are made to turn on the screws and clamp the sides.

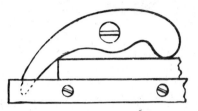

No. 149

This only differs from 148 in being composed of a single pivoted clamp operating in connection with a fixed side-piece.

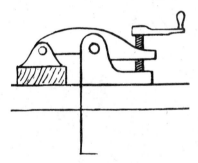

No. 150

A screw-clamp. On turning the handle the screw thrusts upward against the holder, which, operating as a lever, holds down the piece of wood or other material placed under it on the other side of its fulcrum.

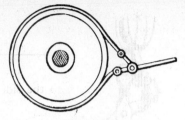

No. 151

A brake used in cranes and hoisting machines. By pulling down the end of the lever, the ends of the brake-strap are drawn toward each other, and the strap tightened on the brake-wheel.

the rope is wound is provided with a flange, B, to which the check-hooks are attached. If the drum acquires a dangerously rapid motion, the hooks fly out by centrifugal force, and one or other or all of them catch hold of the studs, D, and arrest the drum and stop the descent of whatever is attached to the rope. The drum ought besides this to have a spring applied to it, otherwise the jerk arising from the sudden stoppage of the rope might produce worse effects than its rapid motion.

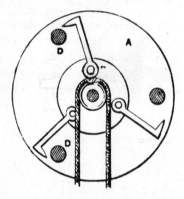

No. 152

Centrifugal check-hooks, for preventing accidents in case of the breakage of machinery which raises and lowers workmen, ores, etc., in mines. A is a frame-work fixed to the side of the shaft of the mine, and having fixed studs, D, attached. The drum on which

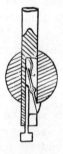

No. 153

A mode of releasing a sounding-weight. When the piece projecting from the bottom of the rod strikes the bottom of the sea, it is forced upward relatively to the rod, and withdraws the catch from under the weight, which drops off and allows the rod to be lifted without it.

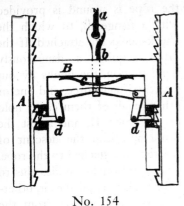

No. 154

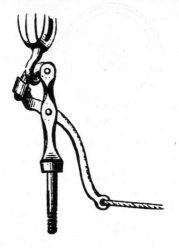

No. 155

C. R. Otis's safety-stop for the platform of a hoisting apparatus. A are the stationary uprights, and B is the upper part of the platform working between them. The rope, *a*, by which the platform is hoisted, is attached by a pin, *b*, and spring, *c*, and the pin is connected by two elbow levers with two pawls, *d*, which work in ratchets secured to the uprights, A. The weight of the platform and the tension of the rope keep the pawls out of gear from the ratchets in hoisting or lowering the platform, but in case of the breakage of rope the spring, *c*, presses down the pin, *b*, and the attached ends of the levers, and so presses the pawls into the ratchets and stops the descent of the platform.

Boat-detaching hook (Brown & Level's). The upright standard is secured to the boat, and the tongue hinged to its upper end enters an eye in the level which works on a fulcrum at the middle of the standard. A similar apparatus is applied at each end of the boat. The hooks of the tackles hook into the tongues, which are secure until it is desired to detach the boat, when a rope attached to the lower end of each lever is pulled in such a direction as to slip the eye at the upper end of the lever from off the tongue, which being then liberated slips out of the hook of the tackle and detaches the boat.

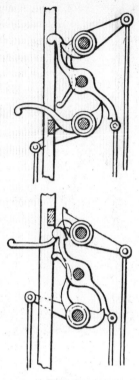

catch and shut the upper eduction and lower steam valves; at the same time, the upper handle being disengaged from the catch, the back weight will pull the handle up and open the upper steam and lower eduction valves, when the piston will consequently descend. *b* represents the position of the catches and handles when the piston is at the top of the cylinder. In going down, the tappet of the piston-rod strikes the upper handle and throws the catches and handles to the position shown in *a*.

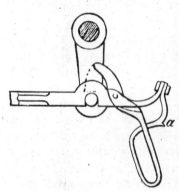

No. 156

Diagonal catch or hand-gear used in large blowing and pumping engines. In *a*, the lower steam-valve and upper eduction-valve are open, while the upper steam-valve and lower eduction-valve are shut; consequently the piston will be ascending. In the ascent of the piston-rod the lower handle will be struck by the projecting tappet, and, being raised, will become engaged by the

No. 157

Apparatus for disengaging the eccentric-rod from the valve-gear. By pulling up the spring handle below until it catches in the notch, *a*, the pin is disengaged from the gab in the eccentric-rod.

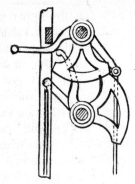

No. 158

Represents a modification of 157, the diagonal catches being superseded by two quadrants.

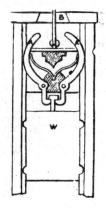

No. 159

Releasing-hook, used in pile-driving machines. When the weight, W, is sufficiently raised, the upper ends of the hooks, A, by which it is suspended, are pressed inward by the sides of the slot, B, in the top of the frame; the weight is thus suddenly released, and falls with accumulating force on to the pile-head.

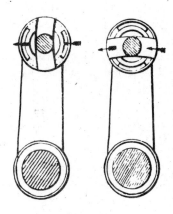

No. 160

Contrivance for uncoupling engines. The wrist which is fixed on one arm of the crank (not shown) will communicate motion to the arm of the crank which is represented, when the ring on the latter has its slot in the position shown in *a*. But when the ring is turned to bring the slot in the position shown in *b*, the wrist passes through the slot without turning the crank to which said ring is attached.

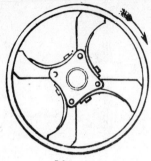

No. 161

Friction pulley. When the rim turns in the opposite direction to the arrow, it gives motion to the shaft by means of the pivoted eccentric arms; but when it turns in the direction of the arrow, the arms turn on their pivots and the shaft is at rest. The arms are held to the rim by springs.

a, *b*, which pulley is loose, and consequently no movement is communicated to the said shafts. When the belt is traversed on the left-hand pulley, which is fast on the hollow shaft, *b*, carrying the bevel-gear, B, motion is communicated in one direction to the upright shaft; and on its being traversed on to the right-hand pulley, motion is transmitted through the gear, A, fast on the shaft, *a*, which runs inside of *b*, and the direction of the upright shaft is reversed.

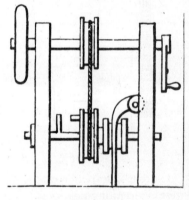

No. 163

Another simple form of clutch for pulleys, consisting of a pin on the lower shaft and a pin on side of pulley. The pulley is moved lengthwise of the shaft by means of a lever or other means to bring its pin into or out of contact with the pin on shaft.

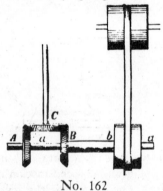

No. 162

A method of engaging, disengaging, and reversing the upright shaft at the left. The belt is shown on the middle one of the three pulleys on the lower shafts,

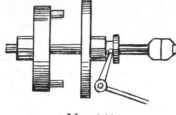

No. 164

Another kind of clutch. The disc-wheel to the right has two holes, corresponding to the studs fixed in the other disc; and, being pressed against it, the studs enter the holes, when the two discs rotate together.

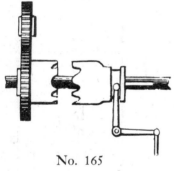

No. 165

Clutch. The pinion at the top gives a continuous rotary motion to the gear below, to which is attached half the clutch, and both turn loosely on the shaft. When it is desired to give motion to the shaft, the other part of the clutch, which slides upon a key or feather fixed in the shaft, is thrust into gear by the lever.

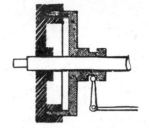

No. 166

A frictional clutch-box, thrown in and out of gear by the lever at the bottom. This is used for connecting and disconnecting heavy machinery. The eye of the disc to the right has a slot which slides upon a long key or feather fixed on the shaft.

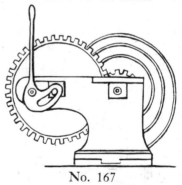

No. 167

Used for throwing in and out of gear the speed-motion on lathes. On depressing the lever, the shaft of the large wheel is drawn backward by reason of the slot in which it slides being cut eccentrically to the center or fulcrum of the lever.

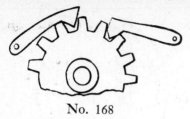

No. 168

An arrangement of stops for a spur-gear.

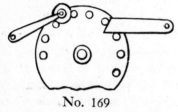

No. 169

Shows two different kinds of stops for a lantern-wheel.

No. 170

Another type of stop. To the driving-wheel, D, is secured a bent spring, B; another spring, C, is attached to a fixed support. As the wheel, D, revolves, the spring, B, passes under the strong spring, C, which presses it into a tooth of the ratchet-wheel, A,

which is thus made to rotate. The catch-spring, B, being released on its escape from the strong spring, C, allows the wheel, A, to remain at rest till D has made another revolution. The spring, C, serves as a stop.

No. 171

B, a small wheel with one tooth, is the driver, and the circumference entering between the teeth of the wheel, A, serves as a lock or stop while the tooth of the small wheel is out of operation.

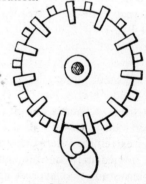

No. 172

Represents a wheel driven by a pinion of two teeth. The

pinion consists in reality of two cams, which gear with two distinct series of teeth on opposite sides of the wheel, the teeth of one series alternating in position with those of the other.

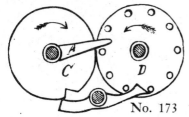

No. 173

The left-hand disc or wheel, C, is the driving-wheel, upon which is fixed the tappet, A. The other disc or wheel, D, has a series of equidistant studs projecting from its face. Every rotation of the tappet acting upon one of the studs in the wheel, D, causes the latter wheel to move the distance of one stud. In order that this may not be exceeded, a lever-like stop is arranged on a fixed center. This stop operates in a notch cut in wheel, C, and at the instant tappet, A, strikes a stud, said notch faces the lever. As wheel, D, rotates, the end between studs is thrust out, and the other extremity enters the notch; but immediately on the tappet leaving stud, the lever is again forced up in front of next stud, and is there held by periphery of C pressing on its other end.

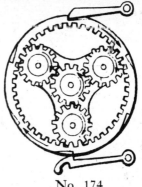

No. 174

Wheel-work in the base of capstan. Thus provided, the capstan can be used as a simple or compound machine, single or triple purchase. The drumhead and barrel rotate independently; the former, being fixed on spindle, turns it round, and when locked to barrel turns it also, forming single purchase; but when unlocked, wheel-work acts, and drumhead and barrel rotate in opposite directions, with velocities as three to one.

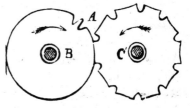

No. 175

The single tooth, A, of the driving-wheel, B, acts in the notches of the wheel, C, and turns the latter the distance of one notch in every revolution of C. No stop is necessary in this movement, as the driving-wheel, B, serves as a lock by fitting into the hollows cut in the circumference of the wheel, C, between its notches.

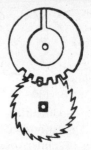

No. 178

Another kind of stop for the same purpose.

No. 176

What is called the "Geneva-stop," used in Swiss watches to limit the number of revolutions in winding-up; the convex curved part, a, b, of the wheel, B, serving as the stop.

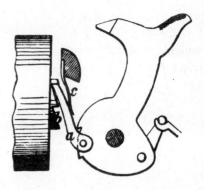

No. 179

Col. Colt's invention for obtaining the movement of the cylinder of a revolving fire-arm by the act of cocking the hammer. As the hammer is drawn back to cock it, the dog, a, attached to the tumbler, acts on the ratchet, b, on the back of the cylinder. The dog is held up to the ratchet by a spring, c.

No. 177

Other modifications of the stop.

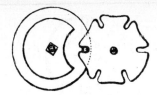

No. 180

Another modification of the stop, the operations of which will be easily understood by a comparison with 176.

No. 181

Arrangement of hammer for striking bells. Spring below the hammer raises it out of contact with the bell after striking, and so prevents it from interfering with the vibration of the metal in the bell.

V.

Special Types of Movement

1. RECIPROCATING AND TRAVERSING MOVEMENT

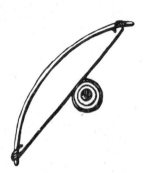

No. 182

Fiddle drill. Reciprocating rectilinear motion of the bow, the spring of which passes around the pulley on the spindle carrying the drill, producing alternating rotary motion of the drill.

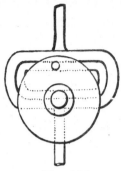

No. 184

Continuous rotary motion of the disc produces reciprocating rectilinear motion of the yoke-bar, by means of the wrist or crank-pin on the disc working in the groove of the yoke. The groove may be so shaped as to obtain a uniform reciprocating rectilinear motion.

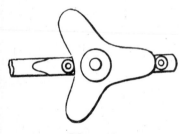

No. 183

Continuous rotary motion of the cam gives a reciprocating rectilinear motion to the bar. The cam is of equal diameter in every direction measured across its center.

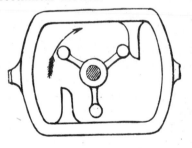

No. 185

A continuous rotary motion of the shaft carrying the three wipers produces a reciprocating rectilinear motion of the rectangular frame. The shaft must revolve in the direction of the arrow for the parts to be in the position represented.

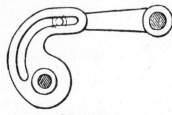

No. 186

A regular vibrating movement of the curved slotted arm gives a variable vibration to the straight arm providing variations of movement thru shaping of slot.

No. 187

By turning the shaft carrying the curved slotted arm, a rectilinear motion of variable velocity is given to the vertical bar.

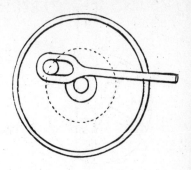

No. 188

The rotation of the disc carrying the crank-pin gives a to-and-fro motion to the connecting-rod, and the slot allows the rod to remain at rest at the termination of each stroke; it has been used in a brick-press, in which the connecting-rod draws a mold backward and forward, and permits it to rest at the termination of each stroke, that the clay may be deposited in it and the brick extracted.

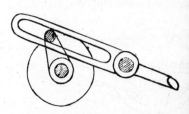

No. 189

Quick return crank motion, applicable to shaping machines.

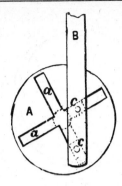

No. 190

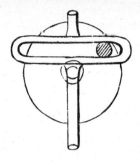

No. 192

Mode of obtaining two reciprocating movements of a rod by one revolution of a shaft, patented in 1836 by B. F. Snyder, has been used for operating the needle of a sewing machine, by J. S. McCurdy, also for driving a gang of saws. The disc, A, on the central rotating shaft has two slots, *a*, *a*, crossing each other at a right angle in the center, and the connecting-rod, B, has attached to it two pivoted slides, *c*, *c*, one working in each slot.

Crank motion, with the crank wrist working in a slotted yoke, thereby dispensing with the oscillating connecting-rod or pitman.

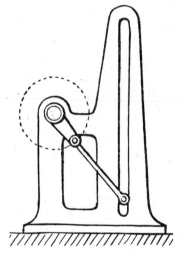

No. 193

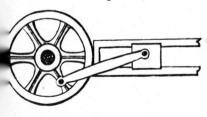

No. 191
Ordinary crank motion.

A means of giving one complete revolution to the crank of an engine to each stroke of the piston.

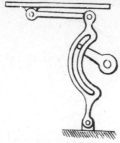

No. 194

Continuous circular into intermittent rectilinear reciprocating. A motion used on several sewing machines for driving the shuttle. Same motion applied to three-revolution cylinder printing-presses.

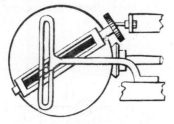

No. 195

A movement used in silk machinery. On the back of a disc or bevel-gear is secured a screw with a tappet-wheel at one extremity. On each revolution of the disc the tappet-wheel comes in contact with a pin or tappet, and thus receives an intermittent rotary movement. A wrist secured to a nut on the screw enters and works in a slotted bar

at the end of the rod which guides the silk on the bobbins. Each revolution of the disc varies the length of stroke of the guide-rod, as the tappet-wheel on the end of the screw turns the screw with it, and the position of the nut on the screw is therefore changed.

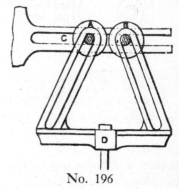

No. 196

A and B are two rollers which require to be equally moved to and fro in the slot, C. This is accomplished by moving the piece, D, with oblique slotted arms, up and down.

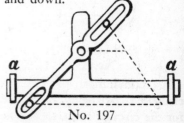

No. 197

Traverse or to-and-fro motion. The pin in the upper slot being stationary, and the one in the lower slot made to move in the direction of the horizontal dotted line, the lever will by its connection with the bar give to the latter a traversing motion in its guides, *a*, *a*.

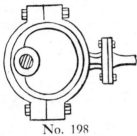

No. 198

An eccentric generally used on the crank-shaft for communicating the reciprocating rectilinear motion to the valves of steam engines, and sometimes used for pumping.

No. 199

A modification of 198, an elongated yoke being substituted for the circular strap, to obviate the necessity for any vibrating motion of the rod which works in fixed guides.

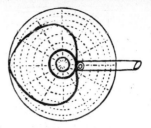

No. 200

A heart-cam. Uniform traversing motion is imparted to the horizontal bar by the rotation of the heart-shaped cam. The dotted lines show the mode of striking out the curve of the cam. The length of traverse is divided into any number of parts; and from the center a series of concentric circles.

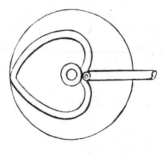

No. 201

This is a heart-cam, similar to 200, except that it is grooved.

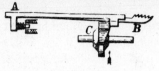

No. 202

Four-motion feed (A. B. Wilson's patent), used on Wheeler & Wilson's, Sloat's, and other sewing machines. The bar, A, is forked, and has a second bar, B (carrying the spur or feeder), pivoted in the said fork. The bar, B, is lifted by a radial projection on the cam, C, at the same time the two bars are carried forward. A spring produces the return stroke, and the bar, B, drops of its own gravity.

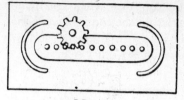

No. 204

What is called a "mangle-rack." A continuous rotation of the pinion will give a reciprocating motion to the square frame. The pinion-shaft must be free to rise and fall, to pass round the guides at the ends of the rack. This motion may be modified as follows:—If the square frame be fixed, and the pinion be fixed upon a shaft made with a universal joint, the end of the shaft will describe a line, similar to that shown in the drawing, around the rack.

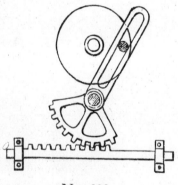

No. 203

On rotating the disc carrying the crank-pin working in the slotted arm, reciprocating rectilinear motion is imparted to the rack at the bottom by the vibration of the toothed sector.

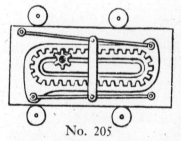

No. 205

A modification of 204. In this the pinion revolves, but does not rise and fall as in the former figure. The portion of the frame carrying the rack is jointed to the main portion of the frame by rods, so that when the pinion arrives at the end it lifts the rack by its own movement, and follows on the other side.

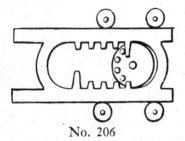

No. 206

Another form of mangle-rack. The lantern-pinion revolves continuously in one direction, and gives reciprocating motion to the square frame, which is guided by rollers or grooves. The pinion has teeth only in less than half of its circumference, so that while it engages one side of the rack, the toothless half is directed against the other. The large tooth at the commencement of each rack is made to insure the teeth of the pinion being properly in gear.

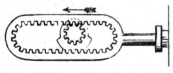

No. 207

C. Parsons's patent device for converting reciprocating motion into rotary, an endless rack provided with grooves on its side gearing with a pinion having two concentric flanges of different diameters. A substitute for crank in oscillating cylinder engines.

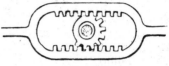

No. 208

Uniform circular motion into reciprocating rectilinear motion, by means of mutilated pinion, which drives alternately the top and bottom rack.

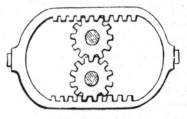

No. 209

Rotary motion of the toothed wheels produces rectilinear motion of the double rack and gives equal force and velocity to each side, both wheels being of equal size.

No. 210

A substitute for the crank. Reciprocating rectilinear motion of the frame carrying the double rack produces a uniform rotary motion of the pinion-shaft. A separate pinion is used for each rack, the two racks being in different planes. Both pinions are loose on the shaft. A ratchet-wheel is fast on the shaft outside of each pinion, and a pawl attached to the pinion to engage in it, one ratchet-wheel having its teeth set in one direction and the other having its teeth set in the opposite direction. When the racks move one way, one pinion turns the shaft by means of its pawl and ratchet; and when the racks move the opposite way, the other pinion acts in the same way, one pinion always turning loosely on the shaft.

which are cut reverse threads or grooves, which necessarily intersect twice in every revolution. A point inserted in the groove will traverse the cylinder from end to end.

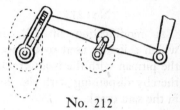

No. 212

The slotted crank at the left hand of the figure is on the main shaft of an engine, and the pitman which connects it with the reciprocating moving power is furnished with a pin which works in the slot of the crank. Intermediate between the first crank and the moving power is a shaft carrying a second crank, of an invariable radius, connected with the same pitman. While the first crank moves in a circular orbit, the pin at the end of the pitman is compelled to move in an elliptical orbit, thereby increasing the leverage of the main crank at those points which are most favorable for the transmission of power.

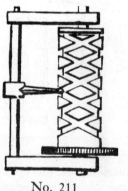

No. 211

Uniform reciprocating rectilinear motion from uniform rotary motion of a cylinder, in

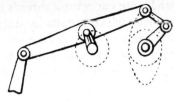

No. 213

A modification of 212, in which a link is used to connect the pitman with the main crank, thereby dispensing with the slot in the said crank.

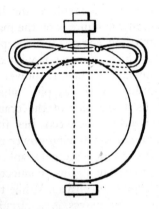

No. 214

A modification of the crank and slotted cross-head, 189. The cross-head contains an endless groove in which the crank wrist works, and which is formed to produce a uniform velocity of movement of the wrist or reciprocating-rod.

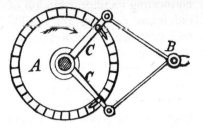

No. 215

Reciprocating rectilinear motion of the rod, B, produces a nearly continuous rotary movement of the ratchet-faced wheel, A, by the pawls attached to the extremities of the vibrating radial arms, C, C.

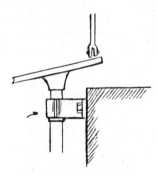

No. 216

On rotating the upright shaft, reciprocating rectilinear motion is imparted by the oblique disc to the upright rod resting upon its surface.

No. 217

A drum or cylinder having an endless spiral groove extending all around it; one half of the groove having its pitch in one, and the other half its pitch in the opposite direction. A stud on a reciprocating rectilinearly moving rod works in the groove, and so converts reciprocating into rotary motion. This has been used as a substitute for the crank in a steam engine.

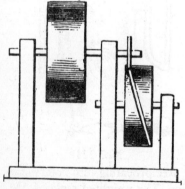

No. 218

Alternating traverse of upper shaft and its drum, produced by

pin on the end of the shaft working in oblique groove in the lower cylinder.

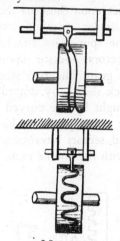

No. 219

Uniform reciprocating rectilinear motion, produced by rotary motion of grooved cams.

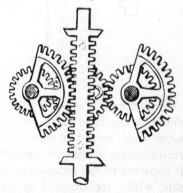

No. 220

Intended as a substitute for the crank. Reciprocating rectilinear motion of the double rack gives a continuous rotary motion to the center gear. The teeth on the rack act upon those of the two semi-circular toothed sectors, and the spur-gears attached to the sectors operate upon the center gear. The two stops on the rack shown by dotted lines are caught by the curved piece on the center gear, and lead the toothed sectors alternately into gear with the double rack.

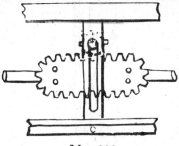

No. 222

Reciprocating rectilinear motion of the bar carrying the oblong endless rack, produced by the uniform rotary motion of the pinion working alternately above and below the rack. The shaft of the pinion moves up and down in, and is guided by, the slotted bar.

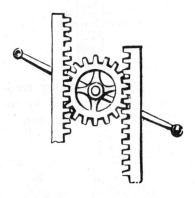

No. 221

Motion used in air-pumps. On vibrating the lever fixed on the same shaft with the spur-gear, reciprocating rectilinear motion is imparted to the racks on each side, which are attached to the pistons of two pumps, one rack always ascending while the other is descending.

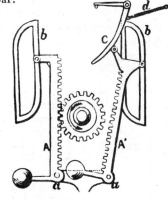

No. 223

Reciprocating into rotary motion. The weighted racks, A, A¹, are pivoted to the end of a piston-rod, and pins at the end of the said racks work in fixed guide-grooves, *b*, *b*, in such manner that one rack operates upon the cog-wheel in ascending and the other in descending, and so continuous rotary motion is produced. The elbow lever, C, and spring, *d*, are for carrying the pin of the right-hand rack over the upper angle in its guide-groove, *b*.

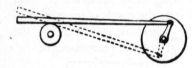

No. 224

Circular into reciprocating motion by means of a crank and oscillating rod.

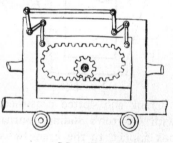

No. 225

The internal rack, carried by the rectangular frame, is free to slide up and down within it for a certain distance, so that the pinion can gear with either side of the rack. Continuous circular

motion of the pinion is made to produce reciprocating rectilinear motion of rectangular frame.

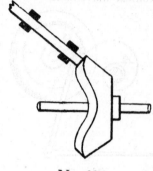

No. 226

Rotary motion of the beveled disc cam gives a reciprocating rectilinear motion to the rod bearing on its circumference.

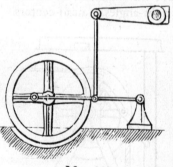

No. 227

Reciprocating curvilinear motion of the beam gives a continuous rotary motion to the crank and fly-wheel. The small standard at the left, to which is attached one end of the lever with which the beam is connected by the connecting-rod, has a horizontal reciprocating rectilinear movement.

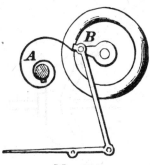

No. 228

A device for assisting the crank of a treadle motion over the dead-centers. The helical spring, A, has a tendency to move the crank, B, in direction at right-angles to dead-centers.

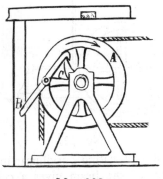

No. 229

A method of working a reciprocating pump by rotary motion. A rope, carrying the pump-rod, is attached to the wheel, A, which runs loosely upon the shaft. The shaft carries a cam, C, and has a continuous rotary motion. At every revolution the cam seizes the hooked catch, B, attached to the wheel, and drags it round, together with the wheel, and raises the rope until, on the extremity of the catch striking the stationary stop above, the catch is released, and the wheel is returned by the weight of the pump-bucket.

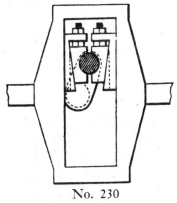

No. 230

Crank and slotted cross-head, with Clayton's sliding journal-box applied to the crank-wrist. This box consists of two taper lining pieces and two taper gibs adjustable by screws, which serve at the same time to tighten the box on the wrist and to set it out to the slot in the cross-head as the box and wrist wear.

2. VARIABLE AND ALTERNATING MOVEMENT

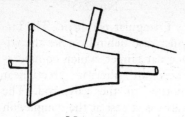

No. 231

Variable motion. If the conical drum has a regular circular motion, and the friction-roller is made to traverse lengthwise, a variable rotary motion of the friction-roller will be obtained.

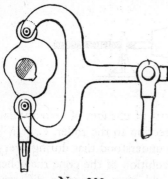

No. 232

Expansion eccentric used in France to work the slide-valve of a steam engine. The eccentric is fixed on the crank-shaft, and communicates motion to the forked vibrating arm to the bottom of which the valve-rod is attached.

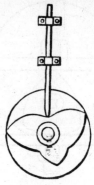

No. 233

On turning the cam at the bottom a variable alternating rectilinear motion is imparted to the rod resting on it.

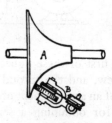

No. 234

Transmission of variable speed for sewing machines. A, driving concave cone. B, swivelling yoke carrying a friction pulley, with a band running a pair of pulleys at the swivel, one of which drives the sewing machine.

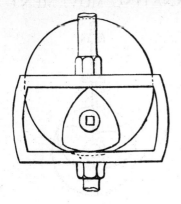

No. 235

Triangular eccentric. The circular disc behind carries the triangular tappet, which communicates an alternate rectilinear motion to the valve-rod. The valve is at rest at the completion of each stroke for an instant, and is pushed quickly across the steam-ports to the end of the next.

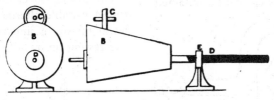

No. 236

The first of these figures is an end view, and the second a side view, of an arrangement of mechanism for obtaining a series of changes of velocity and direction. D is a screw on which is placed eccentrically the cone, B, and C is a friction-roller which is pressed against the cone by a spring or weight. Continuous rotary motion, at a uniform velocity, of the screw, D, carrying the eccentric cone, gives a series of changes of velocity and direction to the roller, C. It will be understood that during every revolution of the cone the roller would press against a different part of the cone, and that it would describe thereon a spiral of the same pitch as the screw, D. The roller, C, would receive a reciprocating motion, the movement in one direction being shorter than that in the other.

No. 237

A cam acting between two friction-rollers in a yoke. Has been used to give the movement to the valve of a steam engine.

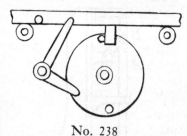

No. 238

Circular motion into alternating rectilinear motion. The studs on the rotating disc strike the projection on the under side of the horizontal bar, moving it in one direction. The return motion is given by means of the bell-crank or elbow-lever, one arm of

which is operated upon by the next stud, and the other strikes the stud on the front of the horizontal bar.

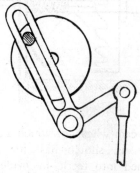

No. 239

Circular motion into variable alternating rectilinear motion, by the wrist or crank-pin on the rotating disc working in the slot of the bell-crank or elbow-lever.

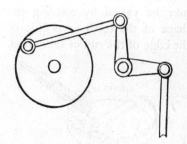

No. 240

A modification of the movement last described; a connecting-rod being substituted for the slot in the bell-crank.

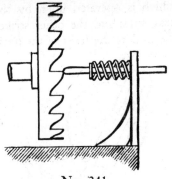

No. 241

A cam-wheel—of which a side view is shown—has its rim formed into teeth, or made of any profile form desired. The rod to the right is made to press constantly against the teeth or edge of the rim. On turning the wheel, alternate rectilinear motion is communicated to the rod. The character of this motion may be varied by altering the shape of the teeth or profile of the edge of the rim of the wheel.

No. 242

Variable circular motion by crown-wheel and pinion. The

crown-wheel is placed eccentrically to the shaft, therefore the relative radius changes.

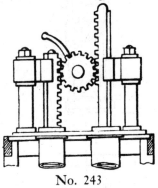

No. 243

By a vibratory motion of the handle, motion is communicated by the pinion to the racks. This is used in working small air pumps for scientific experiments.

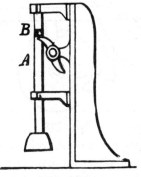

No. 244

Intermittent alternating rectilinear motion is given to the rod, A, by the continuous rotation of the shaft carrying the two cams or wipers, which act upon the projection, B, of the rod, and thereby lift it. The rod drops by its own weight. Used for ore stampers or pulverizers, and for hammers.

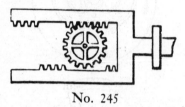

No. 245

Continued rectilinear movement of the frame with mutilated racks gives an alternate rotary motion to the spur-gear.

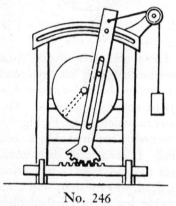

No. 246

By the revolution of the disc in which is fixed a pin working in a slot in the upright bar which turns on a center near the bottom, both ends of the bar are made to traverse, the toothed sector producing alternate rectilinear motion in the horizontal

bar at the bottom, and also alternate perpendicular motion of the weight.

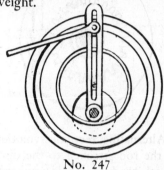

No. 247

Contrivance for varying the speed of the slide carrying the cutting tool in slotting and shaping machines, etc. The driving-shaft works through an opening in a fixed disc, in which is a circular slot. At the end of the said shaft is a slotted crank. A slide fits in the slot of the crank and in the circular slot; and to the outward extremity of this slide is attached the connecting-rod which works the slide carrying the cutting tool. When the driving-shaft rotates the crank is carried round, and the slide carrying the end of the connecting-rod is guided by the circular slot, which is placed eccentrically to the shaft; therefore, as the slide approaches the bottom, the length of the crank is shortened and the speed of the connecting-rod is diminished.

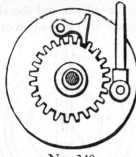

No. 248

Alternating rectilinear motion of the rod attached to the disc-wheel produces an intermittent rotary motion of the cog-wheel by means of the click attached to the disc-wheel. This motion, which is reversible by throwing over the click, is used for the feed of planing machines and other tools.

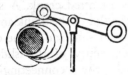

No. 249

A valve motion for working steam expansively. The series of cams of varying throw are movable lengthwise of the shaft so that either may be made to act upon the lever to which the valve-rod is connected. A greater or less movement of the valve is produced, according as a cam of greater or less throw is opposite the lever.

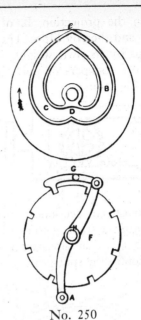

No. 250

These are parts of the same movement, which has been used for giving the roller motion in wool-combing machines. The roller to which wheel, F (Fig. *b*), is secured is required to make one third a revolution backward, then two thirds of a revolution forward, when it must stop until another length of combed fiber is ready for delivery. This is accomplished by the grooved heart-cam, C, D, B, *e* (Fig. *a*), the stud, A, working in the said groove; from C to D it moves the roller backward, and from D to *e* it moves it forward, the motion being transmitted through the catch, G, to the notch-wheel, F, on the roller-shaft, H. When the stud, A, arrives at the point, *e*, in the cam, a projection at the back of the wheel which carries the cam strikes the projecting piece on the catch, G, and raises it out of the notch in the wheel, F, so that, while the stud is traveling in the cam from *e* to C, the catch is passing over the plain surface between the two notches in the wheel, F, without imparting any motion; but when stud, A, arrives at the part, C, the catch has dropped in another notch, and is again ready to move wheel, F, and roller as required.

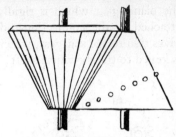

No. 253

Uniform into variable rotary motion. The bevel-wheel or pinion to the left has teeth cut through the whole width of its face. Its teeth work with a spirally arranged series of studs on a conical wheel. One of first differential speed devices.

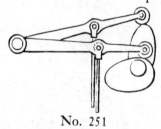

No. 251

Uniform circular converted, by the cams acting upon the levers, into alternating rectilinear motions of the attached rods.

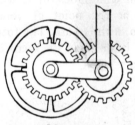

No. 254

Sun-and-planet motion. The spur-gear to the right, called the planet-gear, is tied to the center of the other, or sun-gear, by an arm which preserves a constant distance between their centers. This was used as a substitute for the crank in a steam engine by James Watt, after the use of the crank had been patented by another party. Each revolution of

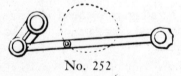

No. 252

A mode of obtaining an egg-shaped elliptical movement.

the planet-gear which is rigidly attached to the connecting-rod, gives two to the sun-gear, which is keyed to the fly-wheel shaft.

No. 255

Represents a mode of obtaining motion from rolling contact. The teeth are for making the motion continuous, or it would cease at the point of contact shown in the figure. The forked catch is to guide the teeth into proper contact.

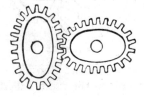

No. 256

Elliptical spur-gears. These are used where a rotary motion of varying speed is required, and the variation of speed is determined by the relation between the lengths of the major and minor axes of the ellipses.

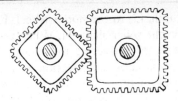

No. 257

Rectangular gears. These produce a rotary motion of the driven gear at a varying speed. They were used on a printing-press, the type of which was placed on a rectangular roller. Continuous rotation of driver produces four progressive accelerations and decelerations of speed in each cycle.

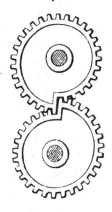

No. 258

Scroll gears to obtain acceleration and deceleration in the cycle.

No. 259

Variable rotary motion produced by uniform rotary motion. The small spur-pinion works in a slot cut in the bar, which turns loosely upon the shaft of the elliptical gear. The bearing of the pinion-shaft has applied to it a spring, which keeps it engaged; the slot in the bar is to allow for the variation of length of radius of the elliptical gear.

turning freely on its center, is carried round by the larger circular disc, which turns on a fixed central stud, which has a pinion fast on its end. Upon the spur-gear is bolted a small crank, to which is jointed a connecting-rod attached to traversing guide-bar. On turning the disc, the spur-gear is made to rotate partly upon its center by means of the fixed pinion, and consequently brings crank nearer to center of disc. If the rotation of disc was continued, the spur-gear would make an entire revolution. During half a revolution the traverse would have been shortened a certain amount at every revolution of disc, according to the size of spur-gear; and during the other half it would have gradually lengthened in the same ratio.

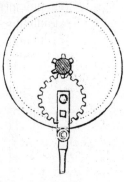

No. 260

Movement used for varying the length of the traversing guide-bar which, in silk machinery, guides the silk on to spools or bobbins. The spur-gear,

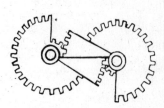

No. 261

A means of converting rotary motion, by which the speed is made uniform during a part, and varied during another part, of the revolution.

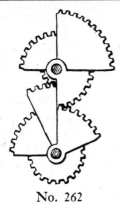

No. 262

An arrangement for obtaining variable circular motion. The sectors are arranged on different planes, and the relative velocity changes according to the respective diameters of the sectors.

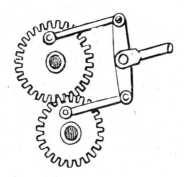

No. 263

The rotation of the two spurgears, with crank-wrists attached, produces a variable alternating traverse of the horizontal bar.

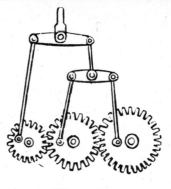

No. 264

A modification of the motion shown in 263, but of a more complex character.

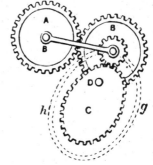

No. 265

Irregular circular motion imparted to wheel, A. C is an elliptical spur-gear rotating round center, D, and is the driver. B is a small pinion with teeth of the same pitch, gearing with C. The center of this pinion is not fixed, but is carried by an arm or frame which vibrates on a center, A, so that as C revolves the frame rises and falls to enable pinion to remain in gear with it, notwithstanding the variation in its radius of contact. To keep the teeth of C and B in gear to a proper depth, and prevent them from riding over each other, wheel, C, has attached to it a plate which extends beyond it and is furnished with a groove, g, h, of similar elliptical form, for the reception of a pin or small roller attached to the vibrating arm concentric with pinion, B.

proper pitching of teeth in a more simple manner than the groove.

No. 267

Mangle-wheel and pinion—so called from their application to mangles—converts continuous rotary motion of pinion into reciprocating rotary motion of wheel. The shaft of pinion has a vibratory motion, and works in a straight slot cut in the upright stationary bar to allow the pinion to rise and fall and work inside and outside of the gearing of the wheel. The slot cut in the face of the mangle-wheel and following its outline is to receive and guide the pinion-shaft and keep the pinion in gear.

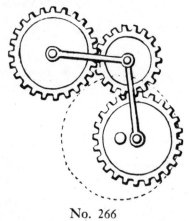

No. 266

If for the eccentric wheel described in the last figure an ordinary spur-gear moving on an eccentric center of motion be substituted, a simple link connecting the center of the wheel with that of the pinion with which it gears will maintain

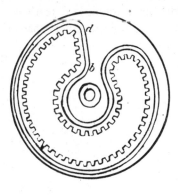

tions of motion, only one circle of teeth being provided on the wheel. With all of these mangle-wheels the pinion-shaft is guided and the pinion kept in gear by a groove in the wheel. The said shaft is made with a universal joint, which allows a portion of it to have the vibratory motion necessary to keep the pinion in gear.

No. 268

A variety of what is known as the "mangle-wheel." One variety of this was illustrated by 36. In this one the speed varies in every part of a revolution, the groove, *b, d,* in which the pinion-shaft is guided, as well as the series of teeth, being eccentric to the axis of the wheel.

No. 270

Another kind of mangle-wheel with its pinion. With this wheel although the pinion continues to revolve in one direction, the mangle-wheel will make almost an entire revolution in one direction and the same in an opposite direction; but the revolution of the wheel in one direction will be slower than that in the other, owing to the greater radius of the outer circle of teeth.

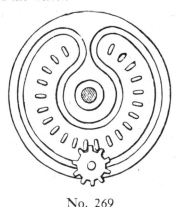

No. 269

Another mangle-wheel. In this the speed is equal in both direc-

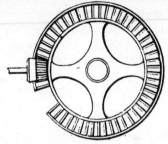

No. 271

Modification of mangle-wheel motion. The large wheel is toothed on both faces, and an alternating circular motion is produced by the uniform revolution of the pinion, which passes from one side of the wheel to the other through an opening on the left of the figure.

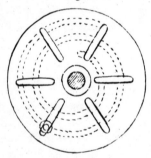

No. 272

Adjustable crank, two circular plates revolving on the same center. In one a spiral groove is cut; in the other a series of slots radiating from the center. On turning one of these plates around its center, the bolt shown near the bottom of the figure, which passes through the spiral groove and radial slots, is caused to move toward or from the center of the plates.

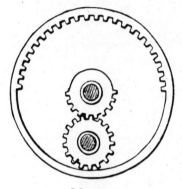

No. 273

The external and internal mutilated cog-wheels work alternately into the pinion, and give slow forward and quick reverse motion.

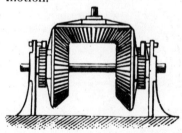

No. 274

Alternate circular motion of the horizontal shaft produces a continuous rotary motion of the vertical shaft, by means of the ratchet-wheels secured to the bevel-gears, the ratchet-teeth of the two wheels being set opposite ways, and the pawls acting in opposite directions. The bevel-gears and ratchet-wheels are loose on the shaft, and the pawls attached to arms firmly secured on the shaft.

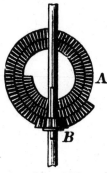

No. 275

Scroll gear and sliding pinion, to produce an increasing velocity of scroll-plate, A, in one direction, and a decreasing velocity when the motion is reversed. Pinion, B, moves on a feather on the shaft.

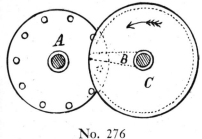

No. 276

The driving-wheel, C, has a rim, shown in dotted outline, the exterior of which serves as a bearing and stop for the studs on the other wheel, A, when the tappet, B, is out of contact with the studs. An opening in this rim serves to allow one stud to pass in and another to pass out. The tappet is opposite the middle of this opening.

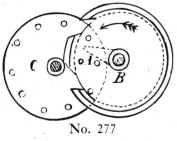

No. 277

The inner circumference (shown by dotted lines) of the rim of the driving-wheel, B, serves as a lock against which two of the studs in the wheel, C, rest until the tappet, A, striking one of the studs, the next one below passes out from the guard-rim through the lower notch, and another stud enters the rim through the upper notch.

This and No. 276 represent what is probably the fore-runner of the gear-wheel. The studs and tappet represent the teeth of gear-wheels.

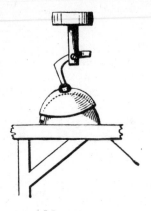

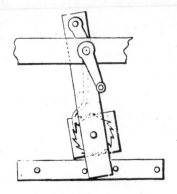

No. 278

No. 279

Contrivance for polishing lenses and bodies of spherical form. The polishing material is in a cup connected by a ball-and-socket joint and bent piece of metal with a rotating upright shaft set concentric to the body to be polished. The cup is set eccentric, and by that means is caused to have an independent rotary motion about its axis on the universal joint, as well as to revolve about the common axis of the shaft and the body to be polished. This prevents the parts of the surface of the cup from coming repeatedly in contact with the same parts of surface of the lens or other body.

Motion for polishing mirrors, the rubbing of which should be varied as much as practicable. The handle turns the crank to which the long bar and attached ratchet-wheel are connected. The mirror is secured rigidly to the ratchet-wheel. The long bar, which is guided by pins in the lower rail, has both a longitudinal and an oscillating movement, and the ratchet-wheel is caused to rotate intermittently by a click operated by an eccentric on the crank-shaft, and hence the mirror has a compound movement.

No. 280

Persian drill. The stock of the drill has a very quick thread cut upon it and revolves freely, supported by the head at the top, which rests against the body. The button or nut shown on the middle of the screw is held firm in the hand, and pulled quickly up and down the stock, thus causing it to revolve to the right and left alternately.

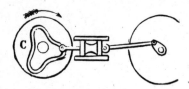

No. 281

Continuous circular motion into intermittent circular—the cam, C, being the driver.

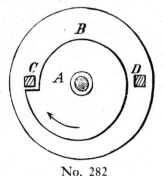

No. 282

Continuous rotary converted into intermittent rotary motion. The disc-wheel, B, carrying the stops, C, D, turns on a center eccentric to the cam, A. On continuous rotary motion being given to the cam, A, intermittent rotary motion is imparted to the wheel, B. The stops free themselves from the offset of the cam at every half-revolution, the

wheel, B, remaining at rest until the cam has completed its revolution, when the same motion is repeated.

No. 283

Triangular eccentric, giving an intermittent reciprocating rectilinear motion, used in France for the valve motion of steam engines.

No. 284

A continuous rotary motion of the large wheel gives an intermittent rotary motion to the pinion-shaft. The part of the pinion shown next the wheel is cut of the same curve as the plain portion of the circumference of the wheel, and therefore serves as a lock while the wheel makes a part of a revolution, and until the pin upon the wheel strikes the guide-piece upon the pinion, when the pinion-shaft commences another revolution.

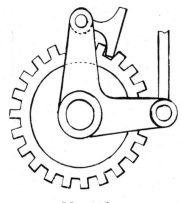

No. 285

Reciprocating rectilinear motion into intermittent circular motion by means of the pawl attached to the elbow-lever, and operating in the toothed wheel. Motion is given to the wheel in either direction according to the side on which the pawl works. This is used in giving the feed-motion to planing machines and other tools.

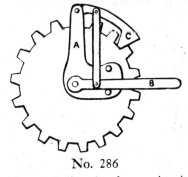

No. 286

Intermittent circular motion is imparted to the toothed wheel by vibrating the arm, B. When the arm, B, is lifted, the pawl, C, is raised from between the teeth of the wheel, and, traveling backward over the circumference, again drops between two teeth on lowering the arm, and draws with it the wheel.

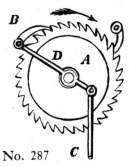

No. 287

Reciprocating rectilinear motion of the rod, C, transmits an intermittent circular motion to the wheel, A, by means of the pawl, B, at the end of the vibrating-bar, D.

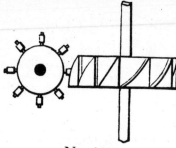

No. 288

Intermittent rotary motion from continuous rotary motion about an axis at right angles. Small wheel on left is driver; and the friction rollers on its radial studs work against the faces of oblique grooves or projections across the face of the larger wheel, and impart motion thereto.

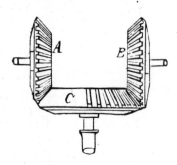

No. 289

A uniform intermittent rotary motion in opposite directions is given to the bevel-gears, A and B, by means of the mutilated bevel-gear, C.

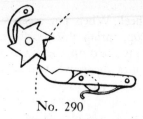

No. 290

The oscillation of the tappet-arm produces an intermittent rotary motion of the ratchet-wheel. The small spring at the bottom of the tappet-arm keeps the tappet in the position shown in the drawing as the arm rises, yet allows it to pass the teeth on the return motion.

No. 291

Jumping or intermittent rotary motion, used for meters and revolution-counters. The drop and attached pawl, carried by a spring at the left, are lifted by pins in the disc at the right. Pins escape first from pawl, which drops into next space of the star-wheel. When pin escapes from drop, spring throws down suddenly the drop, the pin on which strikes the pawl, which, by its action on star-wheel, rapidly gives it a portion of a revolution. This is repeated as each pin passes.

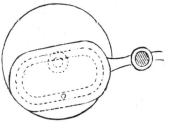

No. 294

Irregular vibrating motion is produced by the rotation of the circular disc, in which is fixed a crank-pin working in an endless groove cut in the vibrating arm.

No. 292

The tilt or trip hammer. In this the hammer helve is a lever of the first order.

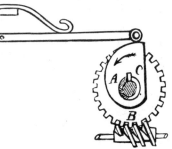

No. 295

An arrangement of jumping motion. Motion is communicated to worm-gear, B, by worm or endless screw at the bottom, which is fixed upon the driving-shaft. Upon the shaft carrying the worm-gear works another hollow shaft, on which is fixed cam, A. A short piece of this hollow shaft is half cut away. A pin fixed in worm-gear shaft

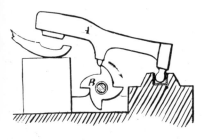

No. 293

Is a tilt-hammer motion, the revolution of the cam or wiper-wheel, B, lifting the hammer, A, four times in each revolution.

turns hollow shaft and cam, the spring which presses on cam holding hollow shaft back against the pin until it arrives a little further than shown in the figure, when, the direction of the pressure being changed by the peculiar shape of cam, the latter falls down suddenly, independently of worm-wheel, and remains at rest till the pin overtakes it, when the same action is repeated.

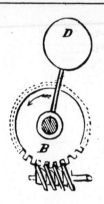

No. 297

A modification of 295; a weight, D, attached to an arm secured in the shaft of the worm-gear, being used instead of spring and cam.

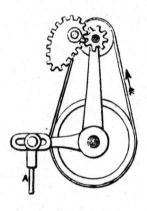

No. 296

A continual rotation of the pinion (obtained through the irregular shaped gear at the left) gives a variable vibrating movement to the horizontal arm, and a variable reciprocating movement to the rod, A.

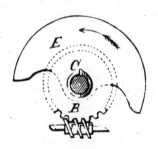

No. 298

A modification of 295; a weight or tumbler, E, secured on the hollow shaft, being used instead of spring and cam, and operating in combination with pin, C, in the shaft of worm-gear.

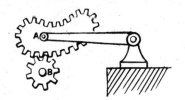

No. 299

The pinion, B, rotates about a fixed axis and gives an irregular vibratory motion to the arm carrying the wheel, A.

No. 300

A nearly continuous circular motion is imparted to the ratchet-wheel on vibrating the lever, *a*, to which are attached the two pawls, *b* and *c*.

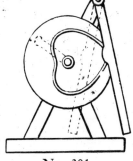

No. 301

The revolution of the disc causes the lever at the right to vibrate by the pin moving in the groove in the face of the disc.

No. 302

Intermittent circular motion of the ratchet-wheel from vibratory motion of the arm carrying a pawl.

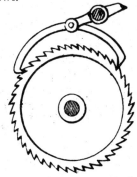

No. 303

A continuous circular movement of the ratchet-wheel, produced by the vibration of the lever carrying two pawls, one of which engages the ratchet-teeth in rising and the other in falling.

two pawls, which act alternately. This is almost a continuous movement.

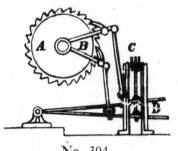

No. 304

On motion being given to the two treadles, D, a nearly continuous motion is imparted, through the vibrating arms, B, and their attached pawls, to the ratchet-wheel, A. A chain or strap attached to each treadle passes over the pulley, C, and as one treadle is depressed the other is raised.

No. 306

A modification of 305.

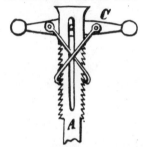

No. 307

Rectilinear motion is imparted to the slotted bar, A, by the vibration of the lever, C, through the agency of the two hooked pawls, which drop alternately into the teeth of the slotted rack-bar, A. This device with adjustable grip to engage drill shank or casing in the drill hole, attached to A was used to withdraw drill or casing from oil wells or test holes in drilling.

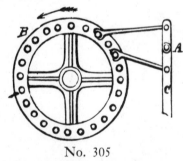

No. 305

The vibration of the lever, C, on the center or fulcrum, A, produces a rotary movement of the wheel, B, by means of the

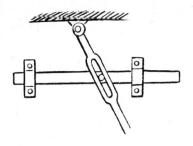

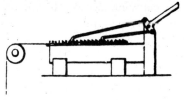

No. 309

On vibrating the lever to which the two pawls are attached, a nearly continuous rectilinear motion is given to the ratchet-bar.

No. 308

Rectilinear motion of horizontal bar, by means of vibrating slotted bar hung from the top.

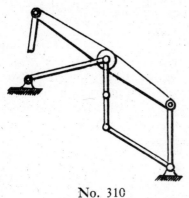

No. 310

A parallel motion.

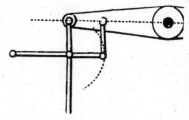

No. 312

A parallel motion commonly used for stationary beam engines.

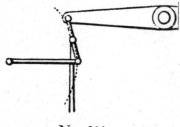

No. 311

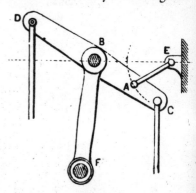

No. 313

Parallel motion in which the radius rod is connected with the lower end of a short vibrating rod, the upper end of which is connected with the beam, and to the center of which the piston-rod is connected.

Another parallel motion. Beam, D, C, with joggling pillar-support, B, F, which vibrates from the center, F. The piston-rod is connected at C. The radius-bar, E, A, produces the parallel motion.

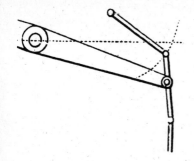

No. 316

Drag-link motion. Circular motion is transmitted from one crank to the other.

No. 314

Another modification, in which the radius bar is placed above the beam.

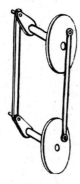

No. 317

The two crank-shafts are parallel in direction, but not in line with each other. The revolution of either will communicate motion to the other with a varying velocity, for the wrist of one crank working in the slot of the other, is continually changing its distance from the shaft of the latter.

No. 315

Circular motion into ditto. The connecting-rods are so arranged that when one pair of connected links is over the dead point, or at the extremity of its stroke, the other is at right angles; continuous motion is thus insured without a fly-wheel.

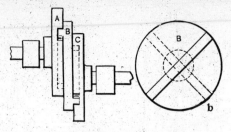

No. 318

"Oldham" coupling for shafts slightly eccentric in alignment. The double-splined disc B runs free against the grooved face plates A, C.

a. Side elevation. b. Front elevation of disc showing grooves at right angles, front and back.

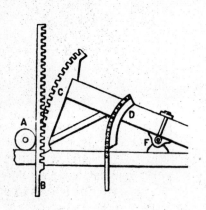

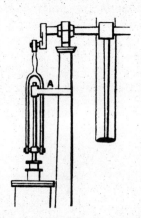

No. 319

Shows a parallel motion used in some of the old single-acting beam engines. The piston-rod is formed with a straight rack gearing with a toothed segment on the beam. The back of the rack works against a roller, A.

No. 320

The piston-rod is prolonged and works in a guide, A, which is in line with the center of the cylinder. The lower part of the connecting-rod is forked to permit the upper part of the piston-rod to pass between.

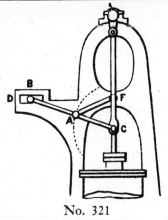

No. 321

Parallel motion for direct action engines. In this, the end of the bar, B, C, is connected with the piston-rod, and the end, B, slides in a fixed slot, D. The radius bar, F, A, is connected at F with a fixed pivot, and at A, midway between the ends of B, C.

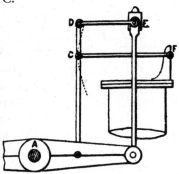

No. 322

A parallel motion used for the piston-rod of side lever marine

engines. F, C, is the radius bar, and E the cross-head to which the parallel bar, E, D, is attached.

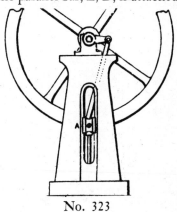

No. 323

A simple means of guiding or obtaining a parallel motion of the piston-rod of an engine. The slide, A, moves in and is guided by the vertical slot in the frame, which is planed to a true surface.

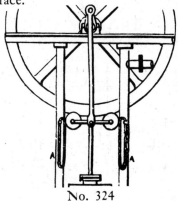

No. 324

Differs from 323 in having

rollers substituted for the slides on the cross-head, said rollers working against straight guide-bars, A, A, attached to the frame. This is used for small engines.

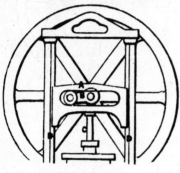

No. 325

An engine with crank motion, the crank-wrist journal working in a slotted cross-head, A. This cross-head works between the pillar guides, D, D, of the engine framing.

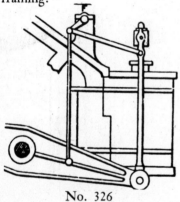

No. 326

An arrangement of parallel

motion for side lever marine engines. The parallel rods connected with the side rods from the beams or side levers are also connected with short radius arms on a rock-shaft working in fixed bearings.

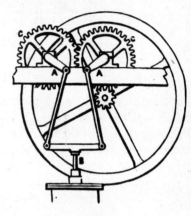

No. 327

A parallel motion invented by Dr. Cartwright in the year 1787. The toothed wheels, C, C, have equal diameters and numbers of teeth; and the cranks, A, A, have equal radii, and are set in opposite directions, and consequently give an equal obliquity to the connecting-rods during the revolution of the wheels. The cross-head on the piston-rod being attached to the two connecting-rods, the piston-rod is caused to move in a right line.

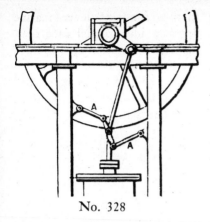

No. 328

Parallel motion for upright engine. A, A, are radius-rods connected at one end with the framing and at the other with a vibrating piece on top of piston-rod.

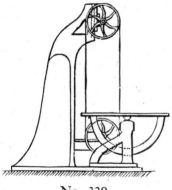

No. 329

Endless-band saw. Continuous rotary motion of the pulleys is made to produce continuous rectilinear motion of the straight parts of the saw.

No. 330

A piston-rod guide. The piston-rod, A, is connected with a wrist attached to a cog-wheel, B, which turns on a crank-pin, carried by a plate, C, which is fast on the shaft. The wheel, B, revolves around a stationary internally toothed gear, D, of double the diameter of B, and so motion is given to the crank-pin, and the piston-rod is kept upright.

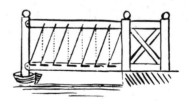

No. 331

Self-adjusting step-ladder for wharfs at which there are rise and fall of tide. The steps are pivoted at one edge into wooden bars forming string-pieces, and their other edge is supported by rods suspended from bars forming hand-rails. The steps remain horizontal whatever position the ladder assumes.

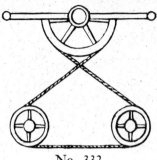

No. 332

By giving a vibratory motion to the lever secured to the semi-circular segment, the belt attached to the said segment imparts a reciprocating rotary motion to the two pulleys below.

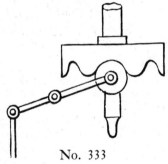

No. 333

Circular into rectilinear motion. The waved-wheel or cam on the upright shaft communicates a rectilinear motion to the upright bar through the oscillating rod.

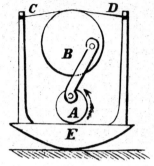

No. 334

Continuous circular motion converted into a rocking motion. Used in self-rocking cradles. Wheel, A, revolves, and is connected to a wheel, B, of greater radius, which receives an oscillating motion, and wheel, B, is provided with two flexible bands, C, D, which connect each to a standard or post attached to the rocker, E, of the cradle.

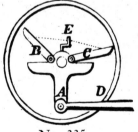

No. 335

Dickson's patent device for converting an oscillating motion

135

into intermittent circular, in either direction. Oscillating motion communicated to lever, A, which is provided with two pawls, B and C, hinged to its upper side, near shaft of wheel, D. Small crank, E, on upper side or lever, A, is attached by cord to each of pawls, so that when pawl, C, is let into contact with interior of rim of wheel, D, it moves in one direction, and pawl, B, is out of gear. Motion of wheel, D, may be reversed by lifting pawl, C, which was in gear, and letting opposite one into gear by crank, E.

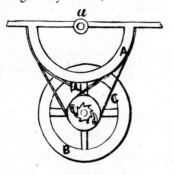

No. 336

Device for converting oscillating into rotary motion. The semicircular piece, A, is attached to a lever which works on a fulcrum, *a*, and it has attached to it the ends of two bands, C and D, which run around two pulleys, loose on the shaft of the fly-

wheel, B. Band, C, is open, and band, D, crossed. The pulleys have attached to them pawls which engage with two ratchet-wheels fast on the fly-wheel shaft. One pawl acts on its ratchet-wheel when the piece, A, turns one way, and the other when the said piece turns the other way, and thus a continuous rotary motion of the shaft is obtained.

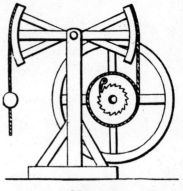

No. 337

Continuous rotary motion from oscillating. The beam being made to vibrate, the drum to which the cord is attached, working loose on fly-wheel shaft, gives motion to said shaft through the pawl and ratchet-wheel, the pawl being attached to drum and the ratchet-wheel fast on shaft.

VI.

Applied Mechanical Movement

1. HYDROSTATIC DEVICES

No. 338

The common pulley and buckets for raising water; the empty bucket is pulled down to raise the full one.

No. 339

Common mode of raising water from wells of inconsiderable depth. Counter-balance equals about one-half of weight to be raised, so that the bucket has to be pulled down when

empty, and is assisted in elevating it when full by counterbalance.

No. 340

Machine of ancient origin, still employed on the river Eisach, in the Tyrol, for raising water. A current keeping the wheel in motion, the pots on its periphery are successively immersed, filled, and emptied into a trough above the stream.

No. 341

Application of Archimedes'

139

screw to raising water, the supply stream being the motive power. The oblique shaft of the wheel has extending through it a spiral passage, the lower end of which is immersed in water, and the stream, acting upon the wheel at its lower end, produces its revolution, by which the water is conveyed upward continuously through the spiral passage and discharged at the top.

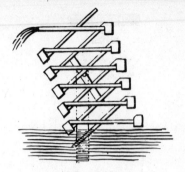

No. 343

Pendulums or swinging gutters for raising water by their pendulous motions. Terminations at bottom are scoops, and at top open pipes; intermediate angles are formed with boxes (and flap valve), each connected with two branches of pipe.

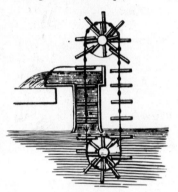

No. 342

Chain pump; lifting water by continuous circular motion. Wood or metal discs, carried by endless chain, are adapted to water-tight cylinder, and form with it a succession of buckets filled with water. Power is applied at upper wheel.

No. 344

Fairbairn's bailing-scoop, for elevating water short distances. The scoop is connected by pitman to end of a lever or of a beam of single-acting engine. Distance of lift may be altered by placing end of rod in notches shown in figure.

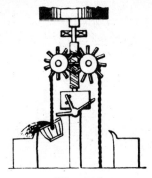

No. 345

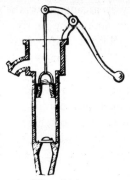

No. 346

Reciprocating lift for wells. Top part represents horizontal wind-wheel on a shaft which carries spiral thread. Coupling of latter allows small vibration, that it may act on one worm-wheel at a time. Behind worm-wheels are pulleys over which passes rope which carries bucket at each extremity. In center is vibrating tappet, against which bucket strikes in its ascent, and which, by means of arm in step wherein spiral and shaft are supported, traverses spiral from one wheel to other so that the bucket which has delivered water is lowered and other one raised.

Common lift pump. In the up-stroke of piston or bucket the lower valve opens and the valve in piston shuts; air is exhausted out of suction-pipe, and water rushes up to fill the vacuum. In down-stroke, lower valve is shut and valve in piston opens, and the water simply passes through the piston. The water above piston is lifted up, and runs over out of spout at each up-stroke. This pump cannot raise water over thirty feet high.

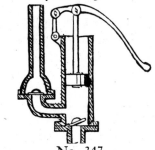

No. 347
Ordinary force pump, with

two valves. The cylinder is above water, and is fitted with solid piston; one valve closes outlet-pipe, and other closes suction-pipe. When piston is rising suction-valve is open, and water rushes into cylinder, outlet-valve being closed. On descent of piston suction-valve closes, and water is forced up through outlet-valve to any distance or elevation.

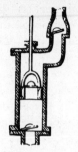

No. 349

Modern lifting pump. This pump operates in same manner as one in previous figure, except that piston-rod passes through stuffing-box, and outlet is closed by a flap-valve opening upward. Water can be lifted to any height above this pump.

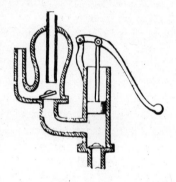

No. 348

Force pump, same as above, with addition of air-chamber to the outlet, to produce a constant flow. The outlet from air-chamber is shown at two places, from either of which water may be taken. The air is compressed by the water during the downward stroke of the piston, and expands and presses out the water from the chamber during the up-stroke.

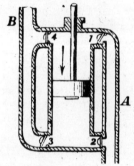

No. 350

Double-acting pump. Cylinder closed at each end, and piston-rod passes through stuffing-box on one end, and the cylinder has four openings covered by valves, two for admitting water and like number for discharge. A is suction-pipe, and B discharge-pipe. When piston moves down, water rushes in at suction-valve, 1, on upper end of cylinder, and that below piston is forced through valve, 3, and discharge-pipe, B; on the piston ascending again, water is forced through discharge-valve, 4, on upper end of cylinder, and water enters lower suction-valve, 2.

No. 352

Balance pumps. Pair worked reciprocally by a person pressing alternately on opposite ends of lever or beam.

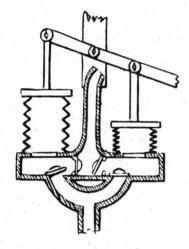

No. 351

Double lantern-bellows pump. As one bellows is distended by lever, air is rarefied within it, and water passes up suction-pipe to fill space; at same time other bellows is compressed, and expels its contents through discharge-pipe; valves working the same as in the ordinary force pump.

No. 353

Bilge ejector (Brear's patent) for discharging bilge-water from vessels, or for raising and forcing water under various circumstances. D is a chamber having attached a suction-pipe, B, and discharge-pipe, C, and having a steam-pipe entering at one side, with a nozzle directed toward the discharge-pipe. A jet of steam entering through A expels the air from D and C, produces a vacuum in B, and causes water to rise through B, and pass through D and C, in a regular and constant stream. Compressed air may be used as a substitute for steam.

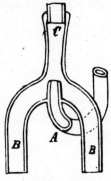

No. 354

Another apparatus operating on the same principle as the foregoing. It is termed a steam siphon pump (Lansdell's patent). A is the jet-pipe; B, B, are two suction-pipes, having a forked connection with the discharge-pipe, C. The steam jet-pipe entering at the fork offers no obstacle to the upward passage of the water, which moves upward in an unbroken current.

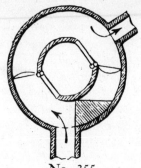

No. 355

Old rotary pump. Lower aperture entrance for water, and upper for exit. Central part revolves with its valves, which fit accurately to inner surface of outer cylinder. The projection shown in lower side of cylinder is an abutment to close the valves when they reach that point.

No. 356

Cary's rotary pump. Within the fixed cylinder there is placed a revolving drum, B, attached to an axle, A. Heart-shaped cam, a, surrounding axle, is also fixed.

Revolution of drum causes sliding-pistons, *c, c*, to move in and out in obedience to form of cam. Water enters and is removed from the chamber through ports, L and M; the directions are indicated by arrows. Cam is so placed that each piston is, in succession, forced back to its seat when opposite E, and at same time other piston is forced fully against inner side of chamber, thus driving before it water already there into exit-pipe, H, and drawing after it through suction-pipe, F, the stream of supply.

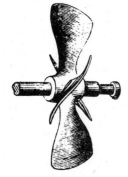

No. 357

Screw propeller. The blades are sections of a screw-thread, and their revolution in the water has the same effect as the working of a screw in a nut, producing motion in the direction of the axis and so propelling the vessel.

No. 358

Hiero's fountain. Water being poured into upper vessel descends tube on right into lower; intermediate vessel being also filled and more water poured into upper, confined air in cavities over water in lower and intermediate vessels and in communication tube on left, being compressed, drives by its elastic force a jet up central tube.

No. 359

Montgolfier's hydraulic ram. Small fall of water made to throw a jet to a great height or furnish a supply at high level. The right-hand valve being kept open by a weight or spring, the current flowing through the pipe in the direction of the arrow escapes thereby till its pressure, overcoming the resistance of weight or spring, closes it. On the closing of this valve the momentum of the current overcomes the pressure on the other valve, opens it, and throws a quantity of water into the globular air-chamber by the expansive force of the air in which the upward stream from the nozzle is maintained. On equilibrium taking place, the right-hand valve opens and left-hand one shuts. Thus, by the alternate action of the valves, a quantity of water is raised into the air-chamber at every stroke, and the elasticity of the air gives uniformity to the efflux.

No. 360

Common paddle-wheel for propelling vessels; the revolution of

the wheel causes the buckets to press backward against the water and so produce the forward movement of the vessel.

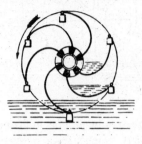

No. 361

Persian wheel, used in Eastern countries for irrigation. It has a hollow shaft and curved floats, at the extremities of which are suspended buckets or tubs. The wheel is partly immersed in a stream acting on the convex surface of its floats, and as it is thus caused to revolve, a quantity of water will be elevated by each float at each revolution, and conducted to the hollow shaft at the same time that one of the buckets carries its fill of water to a higher level, where it is emptied by coming in contact with a stationary pin placed in a convenient position for tilting it.

No. 362

Breast-wheel. This holds intermediate place between overshot
and undershot wheels; has float-
boards like the former, but the
cavities between are converted
into buckets by moving in a
channel adapted to circumference and width, and into which
water enters nearly at the level
of axle.

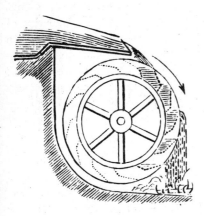

No. 363

Overshot water-wheel

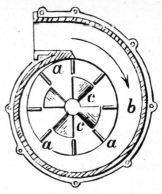

No. 364

Volute wheel, having radial
vanes, a, against which the water
impinges and carries the wheel
around. The scroll or volute casing, b, confines the water in such
a manner that it acts against the
vanes all around the wheel. By
the addition of the inclined
buckets, c, c, at the bottom, the
water is made to act with additional force as it escapes through
the openings of said buckets.

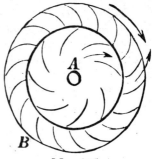

No. 365

A plan view of the Fourneyron

turbine water-wheel. In the center are a number of fixed curved "shutes" or guides, A, which direct the water against the buckets of the outer wheel, B, which revolves, and the water discharges at the circumference.

No. 367

Warren's central discharge turbine, plan view. The guides, *a*, are outside, and the wheel, *b*, revolves within them, discharging the water at the center.

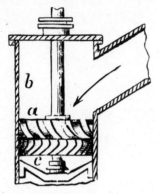

No. 366

Jonval turbine. The "shutes" are arranged on the outside of a drum, radial to a common center and stationary within the trunk or casing, *b*. The wheel, *c;* is made in nearly the same way; the buckets exceed in number those of the shutes, and are set at a slight tangent instead of radially, and the curve generally used is that of the cycloid or parabola.

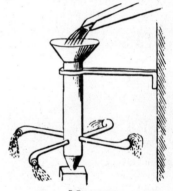

No. 368

Barker's or reaction mill. Rotary motion of central hollow shaft is obtained by the reaction of the water escaping at the ends of its arms, the rotation being in a direction the reverse of the escape.

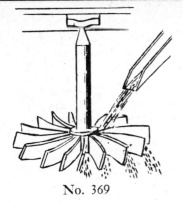

No. 369

Horizontal overshot water-wheel.

action of this ring on the cranks keeps the buckets always upright, so that they enter the water and leave it edgewise without resistance or lift, and while in the water are in the most effective position for propulsion.

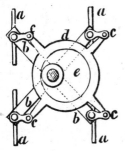

No. 370

Vertical bucket paddle-wheel. The buckets, *a, a,* are pivoted into the arms, *b, b,* at equal distances from the shaft. To the pivots are attached cranks, *c, c,* which are pivoted at their ends to the arms of a ring, *d,* which is fitted loosely to a stationary eccentric, *e.* The revolution of the arms and buckets with the shaft causes the ring, *d,* also to rotate upon the eccentric, and the

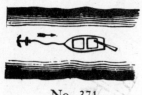

No. 371

This method of passing a boat from one shore of a river to the other is common on the Rhine and elsewhere, and is effected by the action of the stream on the rudder, which carries the boat across the stream in the arc of a circle, the center of which is the anchor which holds the boat from floating down the stream.

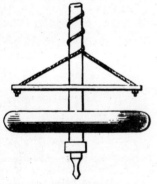

No. 372

Primitive drilling apparatus. Being once set in motion, it is kept going by hand, by alternately pressing down and reliev-

ing the transverse bar to which the bands are attached, causing the bands to wind upon the spindle alternately in opposite directions, while the heavy disc or fly-wheel gives a steady momentum to the drill-spindle in its rotary motion.

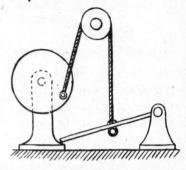

No. 373

A modification of 374, a cord and pulley being substituted for the connecting rod.

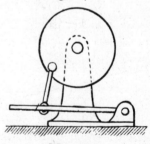

No. 374

Reciprocating curvilinear motion of the treadle gives a circular motion to the disc. A crank may be substituted for the disc.

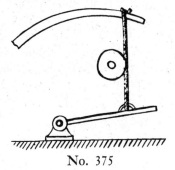

No. 375

Reciprocal motion into alternating circular. When the treadle has been depressed, the spring at the top elevates it for the next stroke; the connection band passes once round the pulley, to which it gives motion.

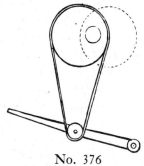

No. 376

Rotary motion of shaft from treadle by means of an endless band running from a roller on the treadle to an eccentric on the shaft.

No. 377

Tread-wheel horse-power turned by the weight of an animal attempting to walk up one side of its interior; has been used for driving the paddle-wheels of ferry-boats and other purposes by horses. The turn-spit dog used also to be employed in such a wheel in ancient times for turning meat while roasting on a spit.

No. 378

The tread-mill formerly employed in jails in some countries

for exercising criminals condemned to labor, and employed in grinding grain, etc.; turns by weight of persons stepping on tread-boards on periphery. This is supposed to be a Chinese invention, and it is still used in China for raising water for irrigation.

The sails are so pivoted as to present their edges in returning toward the wind, but to present their faces to the action of the wind, the direction of which is supposed to be as indicated by the arrow.

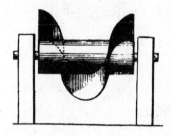

No. 381

A spiral wound round a cylinder to convert the motion of the wind or a stream of water into rotary motion.

No. 379

Common wind-mill, illustrating the production of circular motion by the direct action of the wind upon the oblique sails.

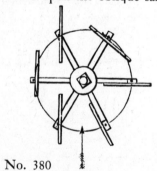

No. 380

Plan of a vertical wind-mill.

No. 382

Fan-blower. The casing has circular openings in its sides through which, by the revolution of the shaft and attached fan-blades, air is drawn in at the center of the casing, to be forced out under pressure through the spout.

No. 383

Æolipile or Hero's steam toy, described by Hero, of Alexandria, 130 years B.C., and now regarded as the first steam engine, the rotary form of which it may be considered to represent. From the lower vessel, or boiler, rise two pipes conducting steam to globular vessel above, and forming pivots on which the said vessel is caused to revolve in the direction of arrows, by the escape of steam through a number of bent arms. This works on the same principle as Barker's mill.

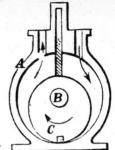

No. 384

One of the many forms of rotary engine. A is the cylinder having the shaft, B, pass centrally through it. The piston, C, is simply an eccentric fast on the shaft and working in contact with the cylinder at one point. The induction and eduction of steam take place as indicated by arrows, and the pressure of the steam on one side of the piston produces its rotation and that of the shaft. The sliding abutment, D, between the induction and eduction ports moves out of the way of the piston to let it pass.

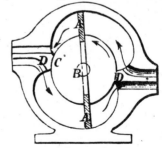

No. 385

Another form of rotary engine, in which there are two stationary abutments, D, D, within the cylinder, and the two pistons, A, A, in order to enable them to pass the abutments, are made to slide radially in grooves in the hub, C, of the main shaft, B. The steam acts on both pistons at once, to produce the rotation of the hub and shaft. The induction and eduction are indicated by arrows.

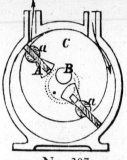

No. 387

Another rotary engine, in which the shaft, B, works in fixed bearings eccentric to the cylinder. The pistons, A, A, are fitted to slide in and out from grooves in the hub, C, which is concentric with the shaft, but they are always radial to the cylinder, being kept so by rings (shown dotted) fitting to hubs on the cylinder-heads. The pistons slide through rolling packings, a, a, in the hub, C.

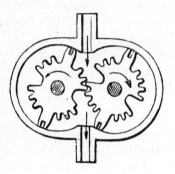

No. 386

Holly's patent double-elliptical rotary engine. The two elliptical pistons geared together are operated upon by the steam entering between them, in such manner as to produce their rotary motion in opposite directions.

These rotary engines can all be converted into pumps.

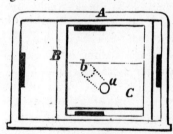

No. 388

Root's double-reciprocating or square piston engine. The "cylinder," A, of this engine is of oblong square form and contains two pistons, B and C, the former working horizontally, and the latter working vertically within it; the piston, C, is connected with the wrist, a, of the crank on the main shaft, b. The ports for the admission of steam are shown black. The two pistons produce the rotation of the crank without dead points.

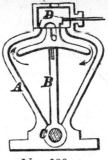

No. 390

Oscillating piston engine. The profile of the cylinder, A, is of the form of a sector. The piston, B, is attached to a rock-shaft, C, and steam is admitted to the cylinder to operate on one and the other side of piston alternately, by means of a slide-valve, D, substantially like that of an ordinary reciprocating engine. The rock-shaft is connected with a crank to produce rotary motion.

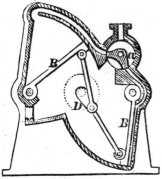

No. 389

Root's patent double-quadrant engine. Two single-acting pistons, B, B, are used, and both connected with one crank, D. The steam is admitted to act on the outer sides of the two pistons alternately by means of one induction valve, a, and is exhausted through the space between the pistons. The piston and crank connections are such that the steam acts on each piston during about two-thirds of the revolution of the crank, and hence there are no dead points.

No. 391

Section of disc engine. Disc piston, seen edgewise, has a motion substantially like a coin when it first falls after being spun in the air. The cylinder-heads are cones. The piston-rod is made with a ball to which the disc is attached, said ball working in concentric seats in cylinder-heads, and the left-hand end is attached to the crank-arm or fly-wheel on end of shaft at left. Steam is admitted alternately on either side of piston.

produced below piston, which is then forced down by atmospheric pressure thereby drawing up pump-rod.

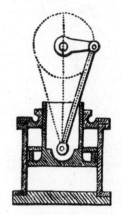

No. 393

Trunk engine used for marine purposes. The piston has attached to it a trunk at the lower end of which the pitman is connected directly with the piston. The trunk works through a stuffing-box in cylinder-head. The effective area of the upper side of the piston is greatly reduced by the trunk. To equalize the power on both sides of piston, high-pressure steam has been first used on the upper side and afterward exhausted into and used expansively in the part of cylinder below

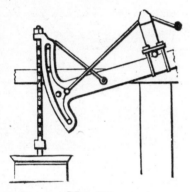

No. 392

Old-fashioned single-acting beam pumping engine on the atmospheric principle, with chain connection between piston-rod and a segment at end of beam. The cylinder is open at top. Very low pressure steam is admitted below piston, and the weight of pump-rod, etc., at the other end of beam, helps to raise piston. Steam is then condensed by injection, and a vacuum thus

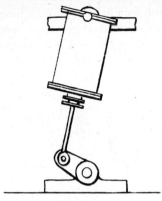

No. 394

Inverted oscillating or pendulum engine. The cylinder has trunnions at its upper end and swings like a pendulum. The crank-shaft is below, and the piston-rod connected directly with crank.

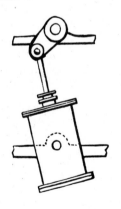

No. 395

Oscillating engine. The cylinder has trunnions at the middle of its length working in fixed

bearings, and the piston-rod is connected directly with the crank, and no guides are used.

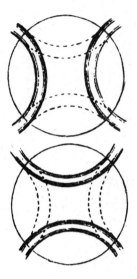

No. 396

Four-way cock, used many years ago on steam engines to admit and exhaust steam from the cylinder. The two positions represented are produced by a quarter turn of the plug. Supposing the steam to enter at the top, in the upper figure the exhaust is from the right end of the cylinder, and in the lower figure the exhaust is from the left—the steam entering, of course, in the opposite port.

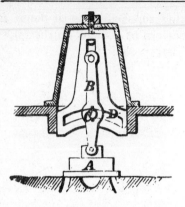

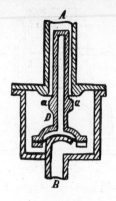

No. 397

Buchanan & Righter's patent slide-valve motion. Valve, A, is attached to lower end of rod, B, and free to slide horizontally on valve-seat. Upper end of rod, B, is attached to a pin which slides in vertical slots, and a roller, C, attached to the said rod, slides in two suspended and vertically adjustable arcs, D. This arrangement is intended to prevent the valve from being pressed with too great force against its seat by the pressure of steam, and to relieve it of friction.

No. 398

Steam trap for shutting in steam, but providing for the escape of water from steam coils and radiators (Hoard & Wiggin's patent). It consists of a box, connected at A with the end of the coil or waste-pipe, having an outlet at B, and furnished with a hollow valve, D, the bottom of which is composed of a flexible diaphragm. Valve is filled with liquid, and hermetically sealed, and its diaphragm rests upon a bridge over the outlet-pipe. The presence of steam in the outer box so heats the water in valve that the diaphragm expands and raises valve up to the seat, a, a. Water of condensation accumulating reduces the temperature of valve; and as the liquid in valve contracts, diaphragm allows valve to descend and let water off.

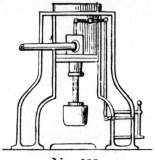

No. 399

Steam hammer. Cylinder fixed above and hammer attached to lower end of piston-rod. Steam being alternately admitted below piston and allowed to escape, raises and lets fall the hammer.

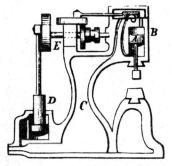

No. 400

Grimshaw's compressed air hammer. The head of this hammer is attached to a piston, A, which works in a cylinder, B, into which air is admitted—like steam to a steam engine—above and below the piston by a slide-valve on top. The air is received from a reservoir, C, in the fram-

ing, supplied by an air pump, D, driven by a crank on the rotary driving-shaft, E.

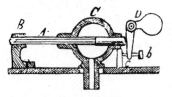

No. 401

Another steam trap (Ray's patent). Valve, a, closes and opens by longitudinal expansion and contraction of waste-pipe, A, which terminates in the middle of an attached hollow sphere, C. A portion of the pipe is firmly secured to a fixed support, B. Valve consists of a plunger which works in a stuffing-box in the sphere, opposite the end of the pipe, and it is pressed toward the end of the pipe by a loaded elbow lever, D, as far as permitted by a stop-screw, b, and stop, c. When pipe is filled with water, its length is so reduced that valve remains open; but when filled with steam, it is expanded so that valve closes it. Screw, b, serves to adjust the action of valve.

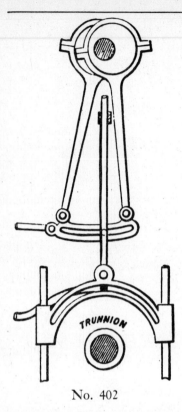

with the cylinder it does not interfere with the stroke of the valve. The two eccentrics and link are like those of the link motion used in locomotives.

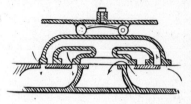

No. 403

Single slide valve, with double steam and exhaust ports. Central steam ports open into steam chest at the side of the valve.

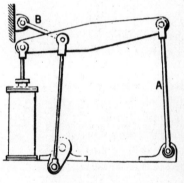

No. 404

"Grasshopper" beam engine. The beam is attached at one end to a rocking-pillar, A, and the shaft arranged as near to the cylinder as the crank will work. B is the radius-bar of the parallel motion.

No. 402

Valve motion and reversing gear used in oscillating marine engines. The two eccentric rods give an oscillating motion to the slotted link which works the curved slide over the trunnion. Within the slot in the curved slide is a pin attached to the arm of a rock-shaft which gives motion to the valve. The curve of the slot in the slide is an arc of a circle described from the center of the trunnion, and as it moves

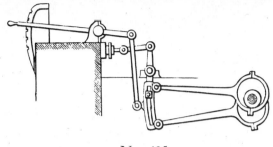

No. 405

Link-motion valve-gear of a locomotive. Two eccentrics are used for one valve, one for the forward and the other for the backward movement of the engine. The extremities of the eccentric-rods are jointed to a curved slotted bar, or, as it is termed, a *link*, which can be raised or lowered by an arrangement of levers terminating in a handle as shown. In the slot of the link is a slide and pin connected with an arrangement of levers terminating at the valve-stem. The link, in moving with the action of the eccentrics, carries with it the slide, and thence motion is communicated to the valve. Suppose the link raised so that the slide is in the middle, then the link will oscillate on the pin of the slide, and consequently the valve will be at rest. If the link is moved so that the slide is at one of its extremities, the whole throw of the eccentric connected with that extremity will be given to it, and the valve and steam-ports will be opened to the full, and it will only be toward the end of the stroke that they will be totally shut, consequently the steam will have been admitted to the cylinder during almost the entire length of each stroke. But if the slide is between the middle and the extremity of the slot, as shown in the figure, it receives only a part of the throw of the eccentric, and the steam-ports will only be partially opened, and are quickly closed again, so that the admission of steam ceases some time before the termination of the stroke, and the steam is worked expansively. The nearer the slide is to the middle of the slot the greater will be the expansion, and *vice versa*.

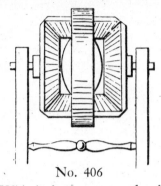

No. 406

White's dynamometer, for de-
termining the amount of power
required to give rotary motion
to any piece of mechanism. The
two horizontal bevel-gears are
arranged in a hoop-shaped frame,
which revolves freely on the
middle of the horizontal shaft,
on which there are two vertical
bevel-gears gearing to the horizontal ones, one fast and the
other loose on the shaft. Suppose
the hoop to be held stationary,
motion given to either vertical
bevel-gear will be imparted
through the horizontal gears to
the other vertical one; but if the
hoop be permitted it will revolve
with the vertical gear put in motion, and the amount of power
required to hold it stationary
will correspond with that transmitted from the first gear, and a
band attached to its periphery
will indicate that power by the
weight required to keep it still.

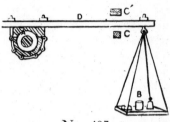

No. 407

A dynamometer, or instrument
used for ascertaining the amount
of useful effect given out by any
motive-power. It is used as follows:—A is a smoothly-turned
pulley, secured on a shaft as near
as possible to the motive-power.
Two blocks of wood are fitted
to this pulley, or one block of
wood and a series of straps fastened to a band or chain, as in
the drawing, instead of a common block. The blocks or block
and straps are so arranged that
they may be made to bite or
press upon the pulley by means
of the screws and nuts on the top
of the lever, D. To estimate the
amount of power transmitted
through the shaft, it is only

necessary to ascertain the amount of friction of the drum, A, when it is in motion, and the number of revolutions made. At the end of the lever, D, is hung a scale, B, in which weights are placed. The two stops, C, C′, are to maintain the lever as nearly as possible in a horizontal position. Now, suppose the shaft to be in motion, the screws are to be tightened and weights added in B, until the lever takes the position shown in the drawing at the required number of revolutions. Therefore the useful effect would be equal to the product of the weights multiplied by the velocity at which the point of suspension of the weights would revolve if the lever were attached to the shaft.

No. 408

Robert's contrivance for proving that friction of a wheel carriage does not increase with velocity, but only with load. Loaded wagon is supported on surface of large wheel, and connected with indicator constructed with spiral spring, to show force required to keep carriage stationary when large wheel is put in motion. It was found that difference in velocity produced no variation in the indicator, but difference in weight immediately did so.

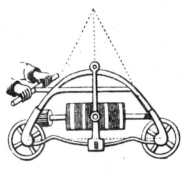

No. 409

Self-recording level for surveyors. Consists of a carriage, the shape of which is governed by an isosceles triangle having horizontal base. The circumference of each wheel equals the base of the triangle. A pendulum, when the instrument is on level ground, bisects the base, and when on an inclination gravitates to right or left from center accordingly. A drum, rotated by gearing from one of the carriage wheels, carries sectionally ruled paper, upon which pencil on pendulum traces profile corresponding with that of ground traveled over. The drum can be shifted vertically to accord with any given scale, and horizontally, to avoid removal of filled paper.

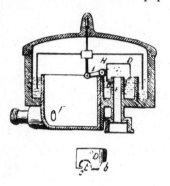

No. 410

Gas regulator (Powers's patent) for equalizing the supply of gas to all the burners of a building or apartment, notwithstanding variations in the pressure on the main, or variations produced by turning gas on or off, to or from any number of the burners. The regulator-valve, D, of which a separate outside view is given, is arranged over inlet-pipe, E, and connected by a lever, d, with an inverted cup, H, the lower edges of which, as well as those of valve, dip into channels containing quicksilver. There is no es-

cape of gas around the cup, H, but there are notches, b, in the valve to permit the gas to pass over the surface of the quicksilver. As the pressure of gas increases, it acts upon the inner surface of cup, H, which is larger than valve, and the cup is thereby raised, causing a depression of the valve into the quicksilver, and contracting the opening notches, b, and diminishing the quantity of gas passing through. As the pressure diminishes, an opposite result is produced. The outlet to burners is at F.

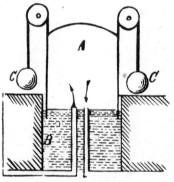

No. 411

Gasometer. The open-bottomed vessel, A, is arranged in the tank, B, of water, and partly counterbalanced by weights, C, C. Gas enters the gasometer by one and leaves it by the other of the two pipes inserted through the bottom of the tank. As gas enters, vessel, A, rises, and *vice versa*. The pressure is regulated by adding to or reducing the weights, C, C.

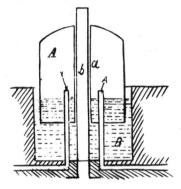

No. 412

Another kind of gasometer. The vessel, A, has permanently secured within it a central tube, *a*, which slides on a fixed tube, *b*, in the center of the tank.

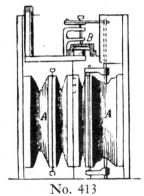

No. 413

Dry gas meter. Consists of two bellows-like chambers, A, A', which are alternately filled with gas, and discharged through a valve, B, something like the slide-valve of a steam engine, worked by the chambers, A, A'. The capacity of the chambers being known, and the number of times they are filled being registered by dial-work, the quantity of gas passing through the meter is indicated on the dials.

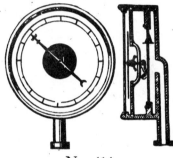

No. 414

Pressure gauge now most commonly used. Sometimes known as the "Magdeburg gauge," from the name of the place where first manufactured. Face view and section. The fluid whose pressure is to be measured acts upon a circular metal disc, A, generally corrugated, and the deflection of the disc under the pressure gives motion to a toothed sector, *e*, which gears with a pinion on the spindle of the pointer.

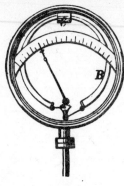

No. 416

Is another contrivance for registering or counting revolutions. A tappet, B, supported on the fixed pivot, C, is struck at every revolution of the large wheel (partly represented) by a stud, D, attached to the said wheel. This causes the end of the tappet next the ratchet-wheel, A, to be lifted, and to turn the wheel the distance of one tooth. The tappet returns by its own weight to its original position after the stud, D, has passed, the end being jointed to permit it to pass the teeth of the ratchet-wheel.

No. 415

Aneroid gauge, known as the "Bourdon gauge," from the name of its inventor, a Frenchman. B is a bent tube closed at its ends, secured at C, the middle of its length, and having its ends free. Pressure of steam or other fluid admitted to tube tends to straighten it more or less, according to its intensity. The ends of tube are connected with a toothed sector-piece gearing, with a pinion on the spindle of a pointer which indicates the pressure on a dial.

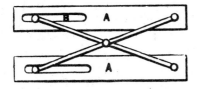

No. 417

Compound parallel ruler, composed of two simple rulers, A, A, connected by two crossed arms pivoted together at the middle of their length, each pivoted at one end to one of the rulers, and connected with the other one by a slot and sliding-pin, as shown at B. In this the ends as well as the edges are kept parallel. The principle of construction of the several rulers represented is taken advantage of in the formation of some parts of machinery.

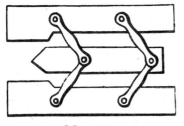

No. 418

Another form of parallel ruler. The arms are jointed in the middle and connected with an inter-

mediate bar, by which means the ends of the ruler, as well as the sides, are kept parallel.

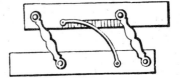

No. 419

A parallel ruler with which lines may be drawn at required distances apart without setting out. Lower edge of upper blade has a graduated ivory scale, on which the incidence of the outer edge of the brass arc indicates the width between blades.

No. 420

Cyclograph for describing circular arcs in drawings where the center is inaccessible. This is composed of three straight rules. The chord and versed sine being laid down, draw straight sloping lines from ends of former to top of latter, and to these lines lay two of the rules crossing at the apex. Fasten these rules together, and another rule across them to serve as a brace, and insert a pin or point at each end of chord to guide the apparatus, which, on being moved against these points, will describe the arc by means of pencil in the angle of the crossing edges of the sloping rules.

jamb; the pencil is secured to arched bar at its connection with cord.

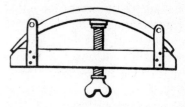

No. 422

Another cyclograph. The elastic arched bar is made half the depth at the ends that it is at the middle, and is formed so that its outer edge coincides with a true circular arc when bent to its greatest extent. Three points in the required arc being given, the bar is bent to them by means of the screw, each end being confined to the straight bar by means of a small roller.

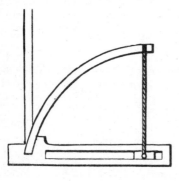

No. 421

Instrument for describing pointed arches. Horizontal bar is slotted and fitted with a slide having pin for loop of cord. Arch bar of elastic wood is fixed in horizontal at right angles. Horizontal bar is placed with upper edge on springing line, and back of arch bar ranging with jamb of opening, and the latter bar is bent till the upper side meets apex of arch, fulcrum-piece at its base insuring its retaining tangential relation to

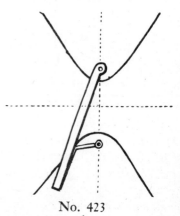

No. 423

Mechanical means of describing hyperbolas, their foci and vertices being given. Suppose the curves two opposite hyperbolas, the points in vertical dotted center line their foci. One end of rule turns on one focus as a center through which one edge ranges. One end of thread being looped on pin inserted at the other focus, and other end held to other end of rule, with just enough slack between to permit height to reach vortex when rule coincides with center line. A pencil held in bight, and kept close to rule while latter is moved from center line, describes one-half of parabola; the rule is then reversed for the other half.

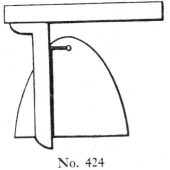

No. 424

Mechanical means of describing parabolas, the base, altitude, focus, and directrix being given. Lay straight edge with near side coinciding with directrix, and square with stock against the same, so that the blade is parallel with the axis, and proceed with pencil in bight of thread, as in the preceding.

No. 425

Proportional compasses used in copying drawings on a given larger or smaller scale. The pivot of compasses is secured in a slide which is adjustable in the longitudinal slots of legs, and capable of being secured by a set screw, the dimensions are taken between one pair of points and transferred with the other pair, and thus enlarged or diminished in proportion to the relative distances of the points from the pivot. A scale is provided on one or both legs to indicate the proportion.

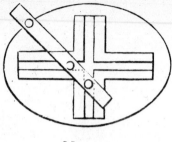

No. 426

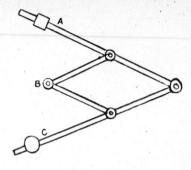

No. 427

An ellipsograph. The traverse bar (shown in an oblique position) carries two studs which slide in the grooves of the crosspiece. By turning the traverse bar an attached pencil is made to describe an ellipse by the rectilinear movement of the studs in the grooves.

Represents a pantograph for copying, enlarging, and reducing plans, etc. One arm is attached to and turns on the fixed point, C. B is an ivory tracing-point, and A the pencil. Arranged as shown, if we trace the lines of a plan with the point, B, the pencil will reproduce it double the size. By shifting the slide attached to the fixed point, C, and the slide carrying the pencil along their respective arms, the proportion to which the plan is traced will be varied.

5. GYROSCOPES

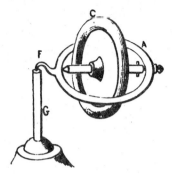

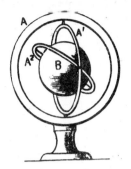

No. 428

No. 429

The gyroscope or rotascope, an instrument illustrating the tendency of rotating bodies to preserve their plane of rotation. The spindle of the metallic disc, C, is fitted to turn easily in bearings in the ring, A. If the disc is set in rapid rotary motion on its axis, and the pintle, F, at one side of the ring, A, is placed on the bearing in the top of the pillar, G, the disc and ring seem indifferent to gravity, and instead of dropping begin to revolve about the vertical axis. This is the principle of the "Sperry" gyroscope now in use.

Bohnenberger's machine illustrating the same tendency of rotating bodies. This consists of three rings, A, A¹, A², placed one within the other and connected by pivots at right angles to each other. The smallest ring, A², contains the bearings for the axis of a heavy ball, B. The ball being set in rapid rotation, its axis will continue in the same direction, no matter how the position of the rings may be altered; and the ring, A², which supports it will resist a considerable pressure tending to displace it.

PART TWO

Mechanical Models

A SERIES OF WORKING MODELS ON THE ART
AND SCIENCE OF MECHANICS

PART ONE of this volume has been devoted to diagrams and descriptions of various applications of the principles of mechanical movement; the following pages contain a series of photographs of actual working models demonstrating these principles.

The exhibit consists of ten panels of sixteen models each; all of which move simultaneously, and demonstrate motion varying in complexity from the simple wedge and inclined plane to the involved radial engine.

To anyone interested in mechanics the operations and construction of these models should be of interest. Each panel is a unit in itself, all sixteen of its models being powered by a single ⅙ horsepower electric motor. The models themselves, constructed of steel, aluminum, brass, and wood, are equipped with ball-bearings and never require lubrication.

Obviously it is not possible to show motion in a photograph, but with a little imagination, it should be possible to visualize the motion that is demonstrated.

The pictures and text in the following pages are reprinted
with the kind permission of the Newark Museum,
Newark, N. J.

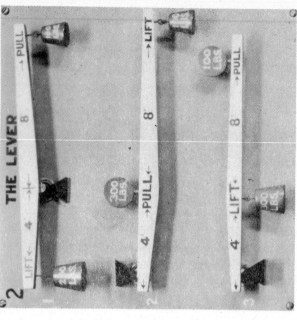

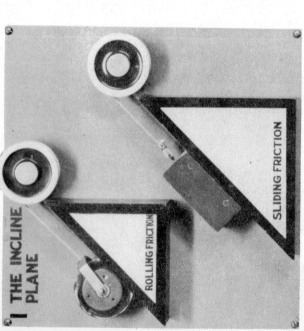

MECHANICAL MODELS

1. INCLINED PLANE. The inclined plane is one of the basic principles of modern machinery. Its chief purpose is to enable a small force to overcome a large force. The act of rolling a barrel up a plank into a wagon is a simple example of the use of the inclined plane. Modifications of this principle are the wedge and screw.

2. LEVER. The lever is another basic principle of mechanics. It consists of a rigid bar resting upon a point called the fulcrum. The points are arranged in model 1 as in pliers and shears, model 2 as in a shovel; model 3 as in the wheelbarrow. The wheel and axle, and pulley are modifications of a lever.

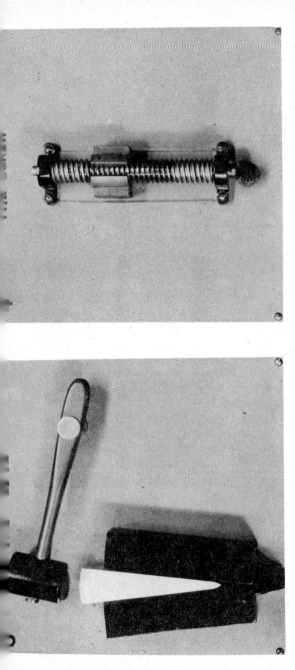

3. WEDGE. The wedge is one of the oldest mechanisms and comes under the heading of the inclined plane. Some examples of wedges are the ax, chisel, nails, pins, carpenter's plane and cutting tools of nearly all kinds.

4. SCREW. From the point of view of the mechanic, the screw is simply an inclined plane wrapped around a cylinder. The vise and letter-press are examples of the screw whose purpose is to obtain increased pressure.

Another example, the jackscrew, is used by builders to lift heavy objects with the least effort. The propellers of boats and airplanes are further examples.

175

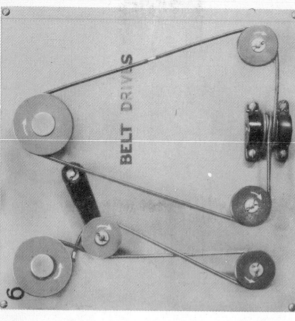

5. BELT DRIVES. Machines are of two kinds—the driving and the driven. Some driving machines are steam and oil engines, electric motors, and water wheels. Examples of driven machines are lathes, drills, planes, and saws. Some connecting link or means of transmission between the two is necessary. A common method is to use belts, chains or cogwheels. By twisting a flat belt half way the shafts may be driven at right angles if the belt rotates as indicated in this specific arrangement. In order to make belt track, center of upper pulley must be in line with right edge of lower pulley. In model 2 reversed motion is obtained by giving the round belt a half turn; and model 3 shows belt in straight line drive with pulleys rotating in same direction.

6. BELT DRIVES. Left hand model shows method of keeping loose belt taut at all times. Other model shows method of transmitting power by round belt in different planes producing the same rotation on the two lower vertical pulleys as indicated by arrows.

7. CHAIN DRIVES. This panel shows early and modern forms of chain drive, the later type on the right being the universally used chain. It is called the silent chain and has small rollers at the contact points, making an almost frictionless performance. The speed of the sprocket wheels is inversely proportional to the number of teeth. Therefore model 1 shows a speed ratio of 1 to 1 and model 2 a ratio of 2 to 1.

8. ROPE DRIVE. Form of pulley used for transmitting power by rope drive, having grooves to prevent slip-ping and to make it a positive drive. The two smaller pulleys below are guide pulleys. Such a drive is used for long distance transmission—example: obtaining power in various sections of an oil field.

177

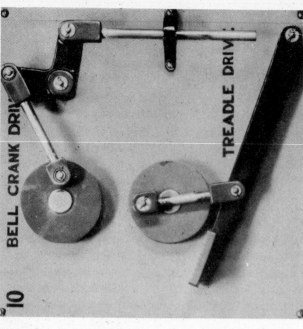

9. PULLEY TYPES. Pulleys are of two kinds, fixed and movable. Both are combined for practical work. These are all fixed pulleys which consist of a wheel with grooved rim, called a sheave, free to rotate on an axle which is supported in a fixed block. A flexible rope or cable passes over

variations in rim to keep the belt from slipping off. The fourth pulley from the left is essentially for a round belt or rope, and because pulley 5 kinks the rope or belt, it is possible to get the greatest pulling power without slipping.

10. TREADLE DRIVE. Treadle drive derived its name from the foot method of obtaining power. The force applied to the treadle is transmitted by the pitman or connecting rod into rotary motion by crank or disc.

BELL CRANK DRIVE. This device makes use of an elbow shaped lever. It is a convenience for transmitting power in different planes as desired.

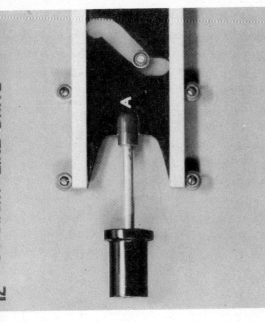

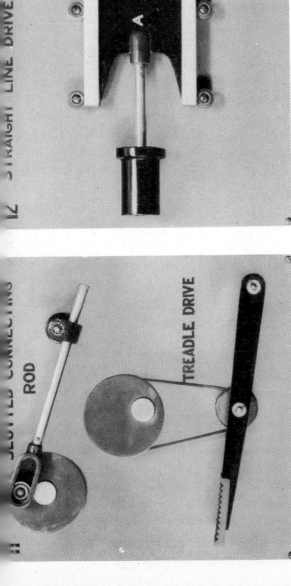

11. SLOTTED CONNECTING ROD. Rotating disk gives motion to rod with pause at both ends of stroke. This is used on brick making machinery. The pause allows mold to be loaded and unloaded at each end of stroke.

TREADLE DRIVE. This treadle drive dispenses with wrist pin used in No. 10 and uses a belt and eccentric or off center pulley.

12. STRAIGHT LINE DRIVE. The straight line motion of A is converted into rotary motion by action of crank B working in an S-shaped slot. This device does away with oscillating motion of rod as in No. 11 (upper,..

179

13   SLOTTED BELL CRANK DRIVE

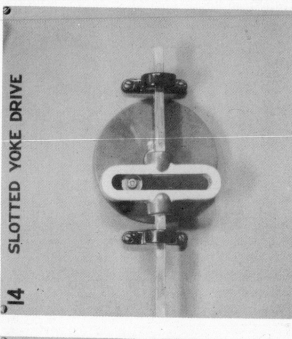

14   SLOTTED YOKE DRIVE

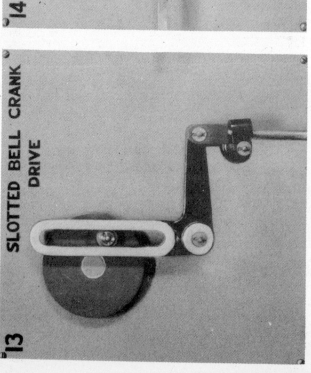

13. SLOTTED BELL CRANK DRIVE. Circular motion of pin in disc, which works inside of the straight, slotted yoke, produces an irregular, vertical motion of rod. Downward motion of rod is slow but has a quick return. Examination of action of rotating pin in yoke explains this.

14. SLOTTED YOKE DRIVE. This is an example of rotary motion being converted into straight line motion. So it is opposite to that of No. 12.

2 TO 1

8 TO 1

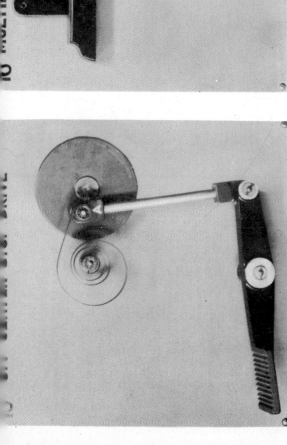

15. OFF-CENTER-STOP DRIVE. This treadle motion has a spring attachment for bringing the crank A, when action ceases, back to a position off center where it will always start when pressure is applied to the foot lever.

16. MULTIPLE TRAVEL MOVEMENTS. Multiple travel movements are very useful. The upper model has a mechanical advantage of 2 to 1 and the lower model of 8 to 1. The latter is that commonly used in expanding gates, doors, etc.

181

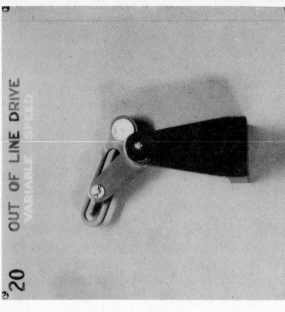

20

OUT OF LINE DRIVE.
VARIABLE SPEED

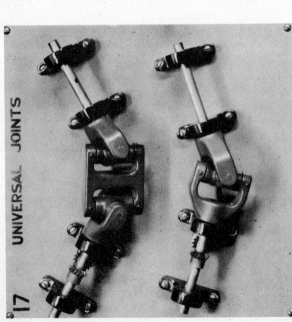

17 UNIVERSAL JOINTS

17. UNIVERSAL JOINTS. A joint is a connecting link between two shafts which are out of line or change position. Its purpose is to transmit power, one end being the driver, the other end being driven, between two shafts which are at any desired angle. A good example of its use is in the automobile where the driven shaft is out of line with the engine or driving power.

20. OUT OF LINE DRIVE. The advantage of this drive is to give a variable speed to the driven shaft to which a rod or other mechanism may be attached. The red slotted arm is the driver and the green crank is driven.

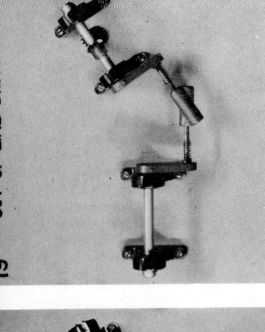

18 and 19. OUT OF LINE DRIVES. The power in these two out of line drives is transmitted by joints. No. 18 is a universal joint but of unusual construction, not as practical as those in No. 17. The joint in No. 19 will only operate when the shafts are placed at the same angle as the angles in the floating tube A, operating between the two driving arms. The placing of the shafts and construction of the tube require great precision.

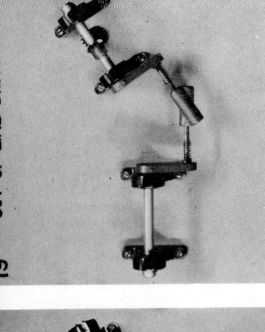

183

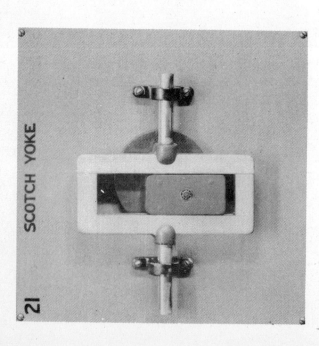

21. SCOTCH YOKE. The green disc carries the driving pin to which is attached a guide, the red block. This guide, working inside of a rectangular yoke, gives a varying speed to the sliding rod, which is slower at the ends than at the center of stroke.

22. ECCENTRIC DRIVE. An eccentric is a revolving disc having the point, on which it revolves, off the center of the disc. The eccentric is the driving force and works in an elongated yoke. This does away with the oscillating motion caused by discs which work in circular guides as in No. 23.

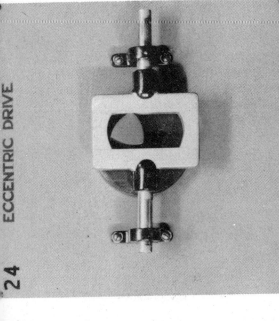

23. ECCENTRIC DRIVE. This type of eccentric is the most commonly used. Application of it can be found in No. 155.

24. ECCENTRIC DRIVE. Attached to the revolving disc in this drive is a triangular cam, which is a projection on a rotating wheel for giving or receiving motion against its edge. In this case, the disc and cam give the mo-

tion. The rod is at rest at the completion of each stroke. This form of eccentric is used on a steam-engine in the Paris Mint.

25. PULLEY LIFTS. Pulleys were described in No. 9. The model on the left is a simple fixed pulley for lifting weights. In this, the power must be equal to the weight to obtain a balance so a one-pound pull is needed to lift a weight of one pound.

The second model has two pulleys, the upper fixed, the lower movable. Since there are two ropes, each exert-

185

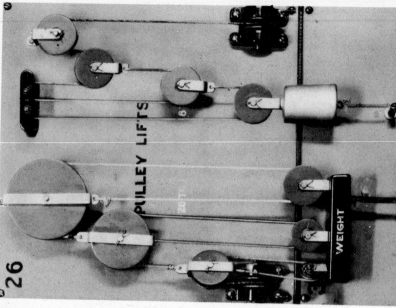

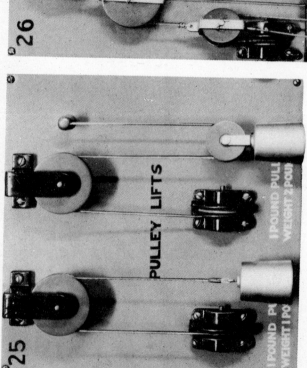

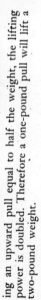

ing an upward pull equal to half the weight, the lifting power is doubled. Therefore a one-pound pull will lift a two-pound weight.

26. PULLEY LIFTS. In this arrangement of pulleys, the mechanical advantage is very high. Note that each cord is attached at one end to a fixed point and to the center of the movable pulley on the other end. The lifting power in the six pulley model (5 movable, 1 fixed) is 26 to 1, and in the four pulley model (3 movable, 1 fixed) it is 8 to 1.

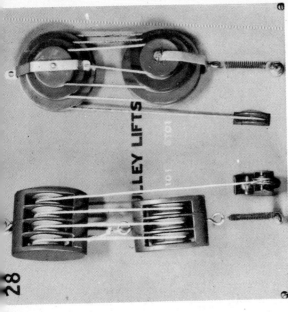

28

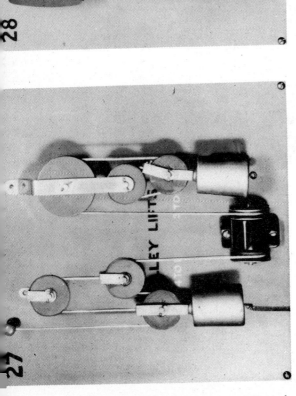

27

27. PULLEY LIFTS. The first model on this panel combines two movable and one fixed pulley. It has a lifting power of 4 to 1 and is generally known as a Spanish barton.

The second arrangement has two fixed and one movable pulley. Its lifting power is 3 to 1.

28. PULLEY LIFTS. Two types of "block and tackle." The first has a lower pulley block with three grooved wheels or sheaves and the upper pulley block has four sheaves. Its lifting ratio is 7 to 1, therefore it will lift seven pounds when one-pound pull is exerted on hand rope. Used most generally in construction work.

The second contrivance is known as White's pulleys, and has a ratio of 6 to 1.

29 RIGHT-ANGLE DRIVE

30 PARALLEL SHAFT DRIVE

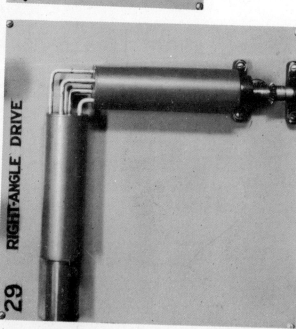

NO DEAD CENTERS

29. RIGHT-ANGLE DRIVE. Between the two revolving drive shafts placed at right angles to one another, are five metal bars bent at right angles. The ends of each are placed in holes in the revolving shafts and are free to be drawn in and out as the shafts rotate. The center is stationary and acts as a guide because it is centered in each shaft. The vertical shaft is the driver in this model. Such a mechanism was used before miter gears were invented.

30. PARALLEL SHAFT DRIVE. This model represents method of driving parallel shafts 1 and 2, without gears and in the same direction. The front and back cranks or arms connected to shafts 1 and 2 are pinned together at a fixed angle. This device has no dead center because while connecting rod A is in line with shafts 1 and 2 (or on dead center) B is in driving position (or off center).

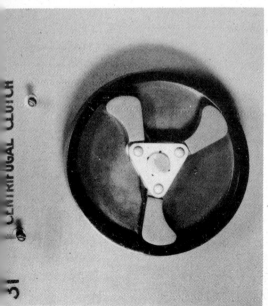

31. CENTRIFUGAL CLUTCH. The shaft carrying the red arms is the driver. When driver is at rest, arms are held back by the springs. When shaft is rotating, the weighted arms expand by centrifugal (from the center outward) force overcoming the pull of springs and engaging the drum so that it is made to move.

32. TOOTHED CLUTCH. A clutch is a mechanical device used to connect a driving and a driven member on the same axis. It is operated by the lever and is designed so that the two members may be engaged or disengaged at will. This type is positive and is used where it is not objectionable to start the driven member suddenly, such as in mowing machines.

33. CONE PULLEYS. Step type. The top pulley is the driver. The rate of speed depends upon the diameter of the pulleys. The lower shaft revolves the slower because the belt is on the small pulley of driver and large pulley of the lower or driven shaft. The speed is reversed when belt is on

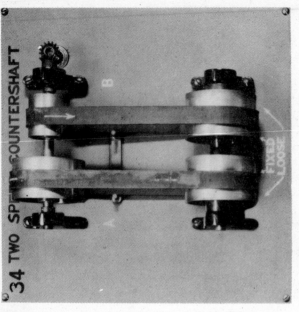

34 TWO SPEED COUNTERSHAFT

33 CONE PULLEYS

large pulley at top and small pulley below.

Variable speed type. The upper cone pulley is the driver and has a constant speed. The position of the belt regulates the speed of the lower cone, making it variable. When the belt is on the left, the speed is minimum and, as it travels along the cone to the right, it increases proportionally as the diameter of the lower

34. TWO SPEED COUNTER SHAFT. This model is so constructed that two speeds may be transmitted by means of belts, the speed being directly proportional to the diameter of the driving pulley. The upper shaft, with a constant speed, is the driver and has two tight pulleys of varying diameters, A being twice that of B. On the lower or countershaft are four pulleys; the two outer ones are loose

and the two inner ones are fixed to the shaft. When the belt on the left is on the loose pulley and is idle, the one on the right is in driving position; therefore a slow motion is transmitted to the lower shaft because the speed obtained is that of the smaller driving pulley above. By shifting the belts, the speed is doubled, because it takes that of the larger driving pulley.

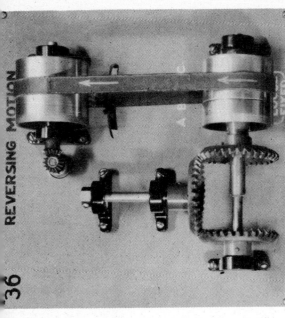

35. TWO SPEED COUNTERSHAFT. No. 35 achieves the same result as No. 34 though the construction is different. The upper shaft is again the driver with a constant speed. On the countershaft are three pulleys, A, B, and C. A and C are fixed, B is loose. Pulley A is connected with the small gear on the left and pulley C with the large gear on the right. When the belt is on pulley B, there is no motion transmitted because the pulley is loose from shaft. When on C, the larger gear rotates and the smaller one below meshes with it. Since the small gear has only one fourth as many grooves as the larger, it must go four times as fast to make a complete revolution with the larger gear. Therefore the speed transmitted to the bottom shaft is maximum. When the belt is on pulley A, the small gear on left rotates, causing the large gear below to mesh with it. Now the speed is reversed because of the relation of these two gears.

36. REVERSING MOTION. Pulleys A, B, and C are arranged like those in No. 35, center loose, and two others fixed. Belt is driven by ·upper shaft and

191

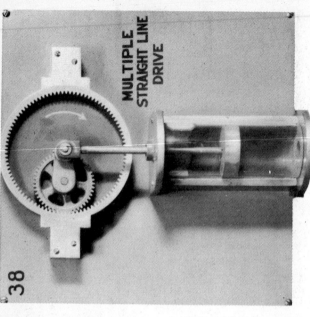

MULTIPLE STRAIGHT LINE DRIVE

STRAIGHT LINE DRIVE

when it drives pulley A, the vertical shaft travels clockwise. Watch meshing of gears. When belt is on pulley B, there is no transmitted motion, and action of belt on pulley C produces a counter clockwise rotation of the vertical shaft. Left hand gear is connected with pulley C, and right hand gear with pulley A. All three

37. STRAIGHT LINE DRIVE. Large fly wheel is on driving shaft, small gear at its center meshes with large gear above which in turn meshes with another gear of equal size. The motion of the two connecting rods attached to these by means of crank arms, brings about a straight line drive on the piston rod.

38. MULTIPLE STRAIGHT LINE DRIVE. This straight line drive is not as forceful as that of No. 37. The small gear driven by crank pin in red disc meshes with the large internal gear, thus increasing the speed. An added advantage of this motion is the great multiplication of the distance traveled by piston rod.

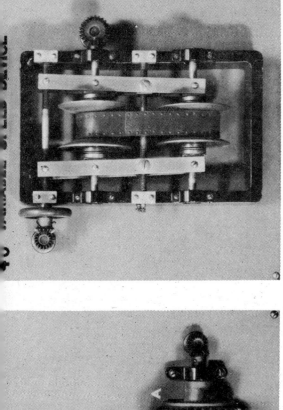

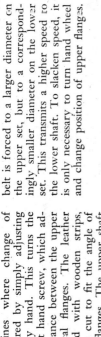

39. REVERSING MOTION. By the use of a toothed clutch, motion is reversed as in No. 36. The lower shaft is driving, and as the clutch member guided by the red arm engages with gear A, the vertical shaft goes clockwise. As gear B is engaged, the motion of vertical shaft is reversed.

40. VARIABLE SPEED DEVICE. This device is used extensively in variable speed machines where change of speed is desired by simply adjusting red wheel by hand. This turns the right and left hand screw, which adjusts the distance between the upper set of conical flanges. The leather belt is faced with wooden strips, having edges cut to fit the angle of the conical flanges. The upper shaft is the driver and when the flanges riding on this are close together, the belt is forced to a larger diameter on the upper set, but to a correspondingly smaller diameter on the lower set. This transmits a higher speed to the lower shaft. To slacken speed, it is only necessary to turn hand wheel and change position of upper flanges.

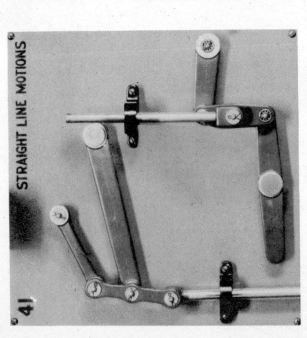

STRAIGHT LINE MOTIONS

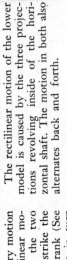

42

ROTARY INTO
RECTILINEAR
MOTION

41. STRAIGHT LINE MOTIONS. With slight variation in construction, two oscillating horizontal arms, if pinned in a straight line with the vertical rod, produce a straight line motion of this rod. This linkage maintains straight line movement where desired.

42. ROTARY INTO RECTILINEAR MOTION.

In both these models, a rotary motion is transmitted into a rectilinear motion. In the upper model, the two studs on the rotating disc strike the elbow shaped arm or bell crank (See No. 10) in rotation and it in turn works between the two studs on the horizontal bar, pushing it back and forth across a field.

The rectilinear motion of the lower model is caused by the three projections revolving inside of the horizontal shaft. The motion in both also alternates back and forth.

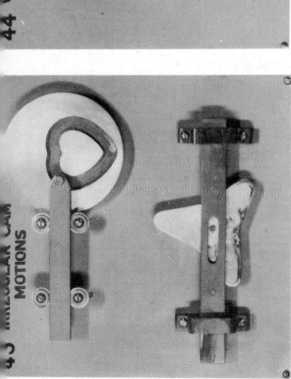

43. IRREGULAR CAM MOTION. The definition of a cam is given in the Glossary. The shape of the cam on this revolving disc determines the motion of the rod on bar. Various shapes may be used, depending upon the special motion required.

The cam in the lower model simply suggests another motion.

44. VARIABLE SPEED AND REVERSE DRIVE. The revolving disc is the driver, transmitting power to shaft carrying vertical wheel. This form of drive does two things—it varies the speed and reverses the motion of the driven shaft. The vertical wheel increases in speed as it is moved away from the center and reverses as it crosses center of driving disc. Such a device has been used on automobiles and does away with shifting gears, but it has not been found practical because of the high friction.

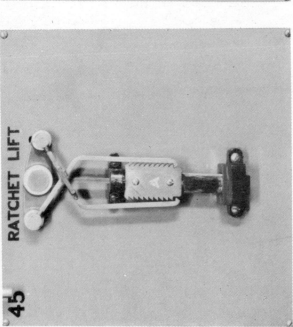

45 RATCHET LIFT

46 RECIPROCATING RECTILINEAR MOTION

45. RATCHET LIFT. As the red lever oscillates, it operates two hooked pawls on the ratchet bar A and lifts the bar. The slot serves as a guide. Used in various ways where it is desirable to hold work at different levels of operation and in fixed position because ratchet only operates in one direction.

46. RECIPROCATING RECTILINEAR MOTION. This combination gives a slow advance and quick return motion to reciprocating bar A. The pin in revolving disc as it changes position working inside the slotted arm causes this reciprocating motion.

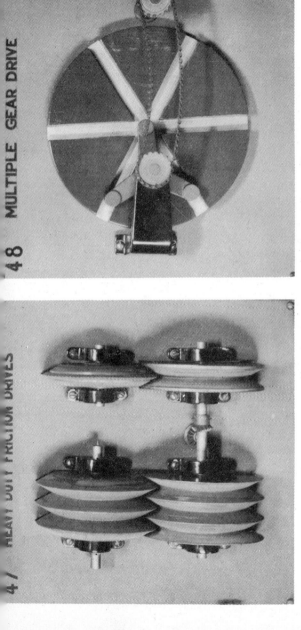

47. HEAVY DUTY FRICTION DRIVES. These drives have a large friction area so that a good grip is made between the two members. These types are used wherever friction drives are necessary.

48. MULTIPLE GEAR DRIVE. This model illustrates a method for reducing speed and obtaining an out of line or off center drive. The shaft carrying the three red arms revolves twice for one revolution of the green slotted disc.

49. RATCHETS, PAWLS AND STOPS. Ratchet mechanisms occur in a great variety of forms. A ratchet consists of a wheel with teeth called the ratchet wheel which receives periodic or intermittent motion from a swing-

197

49 RATCHETS, PAWLS AND STOPS

ing member called a ratch or pawl. Another pawl prevents backward motion; this is called a stop pawl.

Model 1 shows three kinds of stop pawls, each form being necessary to perform its function under different conditions of space in mechanisms to which they are attached. A is the hook type and prevents backward motion by engaging with teeth. B is the straight type and acts as a barrier. Both of these have spring tensions to keep them in place. C is the gravity type, which is held in place by its weight below center.

In Model 2, motion is transmitted to the ratchet wheel by the revolving pawl drive. The stop pawl is of the straight type.

50 PAWL DRIVES AND STOPS

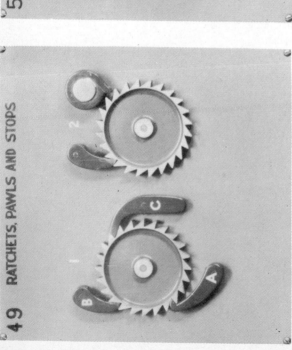

50. PAWL DRIVES AND STOPS. The top model has an almost continuous motion. Watch action of stop pawl. The driver, having both pawls attached to it, acts as both stop and driver alternately.

In the bottom model, the stop and driving pawls are independent. This is used in many ways, particularly in connection with counting devices on automatic machines.

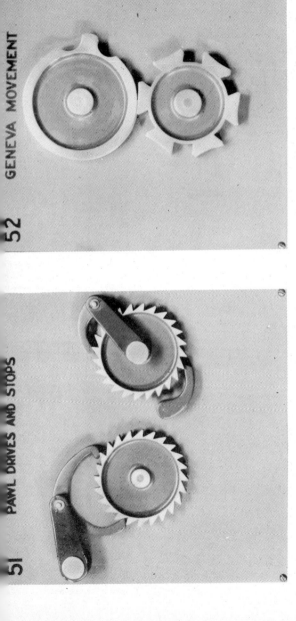

51. PAWL DRIVES AND STOPS. These two types of ratchet movements are used where slow rotations are necessary, such as on feeding mechanisms in textile machinery.

52. GENEVA MOVEMENT. Geneva movement is so called because of its use in Geneva watches as a stop wind. The projection on the driving disc acts as the pawl drive, and the concave projections on the lower disc act as stop pawls. This is used at the present time in motion picture machines for moving the film in front of the lens and is known as the inter- mittent movement. If applied as a stop wind, one of the concave projections must be shaped convex, and the rotation is stopped.

53 CONTINUOUS ROTARY INTO INTERMITTENT MOTION

54 INTERMITTENT FROM CONTINUOUS ROTARY MOTION

53. CONTINUOUS ROTARY INTO INTERMITTENT MOTION. Attached to a revolving disc by means of the green arm, is an elbow shaped lever or bell crank (See No. 10). The pawl, attached to this, drives the notched wheel. The desired direction is attained by placing part marked Reverse on right or left of center.

54. INTERMITTENT FROM CONTINUOUS ROTARY MOTION. The green wheel on horizontal shaft is driving the vertical shaft at right angles through the medium of the toothed drum. The motion of the driver is continuous but that of the drum is intermittent because there is a slight pause between the time a projection on the driver leaves one groove on the drum and enters the next.

55. CAM WHEEL FOR INTERMITTENT MOTION. The cam as previously explained is a projection on a rotating wheel for giving or receiving motion against its edge (See No. 24). The shape and size of this edge determines the resultant motion of the follower, which is the rod working through guides. This model is so constructed that the constant rotary motion of the cam wheel is converted into intermittent vertical motion.

56. WAVE WHEEL FOR OSCILLATING MOTION. There is great similarity between this model and No. 55. No. 56 shows three types of motion: continuous rotary as in the wave wheel, oscillating or swinging as in the lever, and intermittent as in the rod.

201

57. JUMP MOTION DEVICE. The main parts of this device are the worm wheel (above) and worm gear (below). The motion of the worm wheel is continuous because it is on the driving shaft. The teeth on the vertical worm gear mesh with the horizontal worm wheel. When the gear has revolved sufficiently to escape contact on the worm wheel, the red weight (by gravity) advances the gear very quickly to meet the worm and repeat the process. In one cycle, the motion is controlled to be slow when meshing with gear, and very fast when jumping.

58. RATCHET AND PAWL MOVEMENT. This is a step ratchet for heavy duty and is very commonly used for pipe cutting dies, ratchet wrenches, etc.

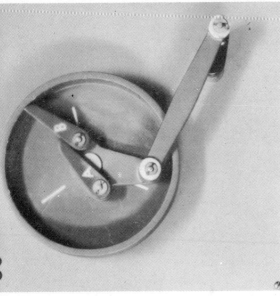

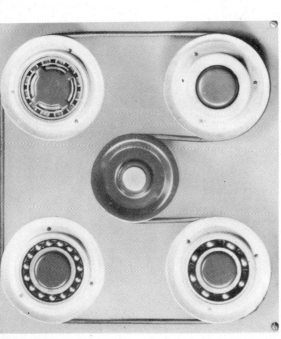

59. BALL BEARINGS AND ROLLER BEARINGS.
Bearings are the supports for rotating members or shafts and the term as generally applied includes the whole support. The friction caused by the moving body in the bearing has always been a great problem, until the introduction of ball and roller bearings which are called anti-friction bearings.

The two models on the left employ balls and those on the right use rollers. In all cases, the outer shell rotating on the axle carries the load and the axle is represented by tne red center.

60. OSCILLATING INTO INTERMITTENT CIRCULAR MOTION. The kind of motion
and its direction in this model are dependent upon the position of the two green arms, A and B. The rotation of the crank arm which is attached to the driving shaft gives an oscillating motion to the connecting rod, at the other end of which is another crank arm pinned to the center of the rotating disc. If A en-

203

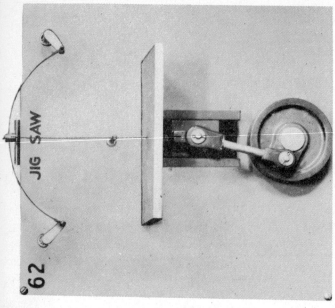

62 JIG SAW

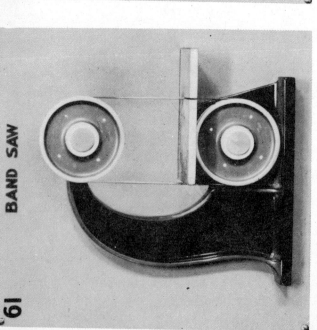

61 BAND SAW

gages the drum, the resulting motion is intermittent and clockwise; if B engages the drum, the direction is reversed; and if both A and B touch the drum it oscillates in one position.

61. BAND SAW. The constant rotary motion of the driving pulley (lower) produces a continuous straight line motion of the straight parts of the saw. The upper pulley is a guide. This type is used at high speed for cutting wood or other substances. When run at low speed with high-tempered steel it is used on metals.

62. JIG SAW. The vertical saw is drawn down by crank pin, cutting material, and is then drawn back by tension of spring above. This type is used for sawing irregular shapes in wood and later the band saw was developed from it. It is possible to saw inside of a form by placing the saw blade through a hole in the work before fastening to spring. When job is complete, saw is loosened and work slipped off.

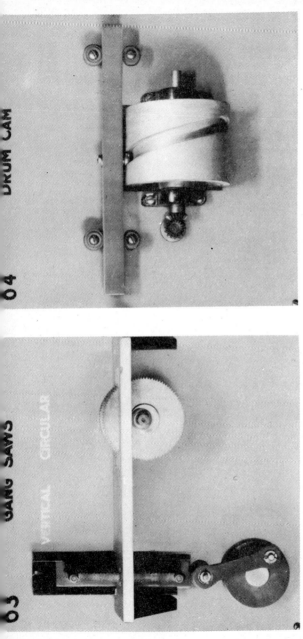

VERTICAL   CIRCULAR

63. GANG SAWS, vertical and circular types. The word gang is used when more than one saw is combined to operate at the same time. In the vertical type the power is supplied by a pin on the rotating red disc. A connecting rod is used to transmit the power. This type is used to cut on down stroke only.

The driving shaft runs through the circular saw so the power is directly applied. This type was developed after the vertical and produces a continuous cutting motion. It is the most used now and will saw a log with one cutting, depending on number of saws used.

64. DRUM CAM. This shows another way in which a cam may be used. The intermittent motion given to the traveling arm depends on the angle or shape of groove in drum. This motion can be worked into many combinations and is used in numberless ways, particularly on automatic screw-cutting machines.

205

SPUR GEARS

SPEED 18—30

DRIVER→ →DRIVEN

MOTION IN OPPOSITE DIRECTIONS

SQUARE GEARS

DRIVER→

DRIVEN→

VARIABLE SPEED

65. SPUR GEARS. Gears are used to transmit power from one shaft to another and are now used in practically every complicated machine. There are a variety of types.

This model shows ordinary spur gears, having grooves parallel to the shaft. When the large gear is the driver the small one is driven at a greater speed, having eighteen teeth to the thirty of the driving gear. When the small gear is the driver, the large one revolves at a correspondingly slower speed.

66. SQUARE GEARS. This type of gearing transmits a variable speed. The top gear is the driver and has a constant speed. The lower gear runs slow when the corners are up in position and faster when driver engages the flat sides. This type is not commonly used.

DRIVER→

DRIVEN→

VARIABLE SPEED

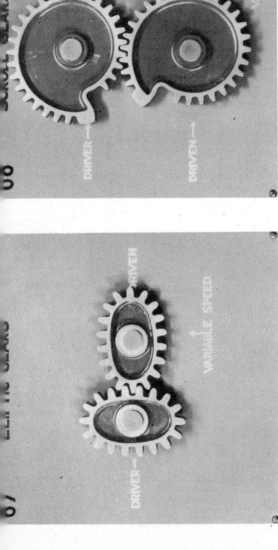

DRIVER→

DRIVEN

VARIABLE SPEED

67. ELLIPTIC GEARS. These are the most common of the non-circular gears. Left gear running constant, drives right gear at a variable speed depending upon the shape of the el-lipse. Used in certain types of printing presses.

68. SCROLL GEARS. This type of gearing produces a gradually increasing and decreasing speed during one revo-lution. The speed of driven gear is slowest when its longest point from center is engaged with driver. There are a variety of scroll gears to suit the condition of motion required.

207

69 INTERNAL AND SPUR GEARS

MOTION SAME DIRECTION

70 REVERSE FROM ROTARY MOTION

69. INTERNAL AND SPUR GEARS. This shows two types of gears, internal and external spur gears in combination. Note that the large internal gear is driving a small spur gear and both are turning in the same direction. Referring to No. 65, you will see that spur gears in combination turn in opposite directions. Application of this combination may be found in No. 70.

70. REVERSE FROM ROTARY MOTION. There are three gears in combination in this model—internal, spur, and mutilated gear in center. The large or internal gear and mutilated gear are both drivers. When the teeth on the internal gear mesh with the teeth on the small spur gear the motion is in one direction. When teeth in the mutilated gear mesh with spur gear the action is reversed. The red target disc indicates this. Motion is transmitted to the target disc by a chain drive (See No. 7.) This movement is usable in any type of machine where advance is slow and return fast or vice versa.

72 WORM AND GEAR

SPEED REDUCTION OR MULTIPLYING POWER

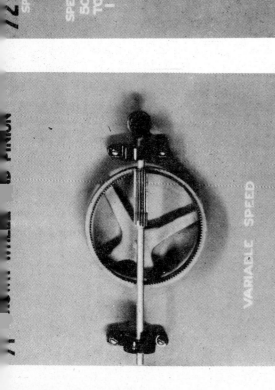

VARIABLE SPEED

71. CROWN WHEEL AND PINION. The cogwheel or pinion rotating on the horizontal shaft is driving the large crown wheel. The pinion runs at constant speed because it is on the driving shaft but that of the crown wheel varies at every point from slower to faster movement because it rotates on a point off-center.

72. WORM AND GEAR. The worm or continuous screw on the horizontal shaft is the driver. This combination reduces the speed of the driven member and also multiplies its power. The power increases proportionally as the speed decreases. The speed ratio of shafts depends upon the relation of number of threads on the worm (single or multiple) to the number of teeth in the worm wheel or gear. This type of speed reducer is used between shafts at right angles to each other.

209

73 MITER AND BEVEL GEARS

SPIRAL GEARS   HELICAL MITERS

BEVEL GEARS   PLAIN MITERS

74 WORMS AND GEARS

73. MITER AND BEVEL GEARS. The miter gears are the two models on the right. Miter gears are used to transmit motion between two shafts placed at right angles to each other. Since the gears are of equal diameter, they both revolve at the same speed. The angle of the grooves to the shaft is 45° in all miter gears. Helical miters are so cut that they are noiseless. Therefore they are used for high speed trans-

The lower model on the left shows the action of bevel gears. Bevel gears also run at right angles to each other but the two gears in combination are of different sizes. Since the speed transmitted is different these gears are used when a differential speed is desired. The angle of the teeth depends on the diameter of the two gears.

The spiral gears are developed primarily for automobile drives but are

chinery.

74. WORMS AND GEARS. This combination shows the method of changing rotation of driven gear. Note the right and left-hand angle of the threads in the continuous screw or worm. Teeth in lower gears have corresponding left and right angles. The threads of these worms are of the multiple type and have five leads while that in No. 72 is a single thread, having only one

75. VARIABLE SPEED GEARS. In this combination of gears there are two speeds and a stop movement due to the relation of the diameters of the parts that mesh. When the teeth of equal diameters are meshed, as on black sectors, both gears turn at the same speed. But when red sectors are in mesh the speed of the lower gear is doubled because it has a diameter of four inches while that of the upper projection is eight inches. When no gears mesh, there is a stop in the rotation of the lower gear.

76. MULTIPLE SPEED DRIVE. When more than two gears are in mesh such a combination is a train of mechanisms and is called a gear train or a train of gears. This train of gears is of a special type called epicyclic, because the one on the left is fixed and the horizontal gear is carried on a shaft which rotates about the axis of the fixed gear. The gear on the right is attached to the driven shaft and is made to rotate at double speed, teeing the sum of two movements of the horizontal gear, its rotation on its own axis and its meshing with the fixed gear about which it rotates.

211

77 SWASH PLATE GEARS

78 VARIABLE RECIPROCATING MOVEMENT

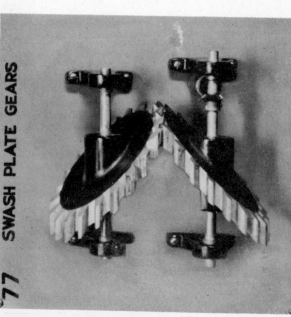

77. SWASH PLATE GEARS. This combination of gears is unusual and the only known application was in a dough-mixing machine. The action is identical with two plain spur gears of same diameter. Close observation will show that the teeth are cut parallel with the shafts and all are the same distance from their respective centers. Take a diagonal slice from a great length of a spur gear, and the result is a swash plate gear.

78. VARIABLE RECIPROCATING MOVEMENT. The combination of gearing in this model produces a variable speed and movement of the lever and arm. Many different combinations are worked out in this manner. A particular use is in textile machinery.

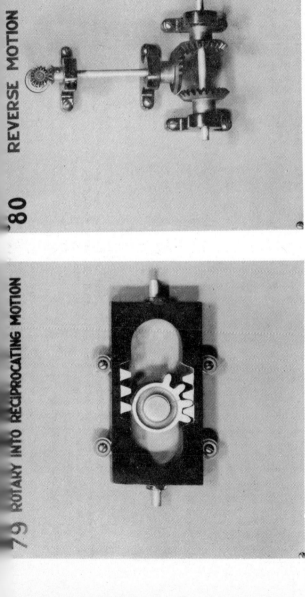

79. ROTARY INTO RECIPROCATING MOTION. The constant rotation of the four-toothed wheel inside of a specially constructed rack gives the reciprocating motion to the shaft through alternate meshing of the teeth on rack.

80. REVERSE MOTION. The reverse motion of the driven shaft is caused by the meshing of a mutilated bevel gear with two bevel gears at right angles to it. It is also caused because the meshing of the gears is on opposite sides of the driver. The motion of both the driving and driven shafts is rotary. Compare action to that in No. 39.

213

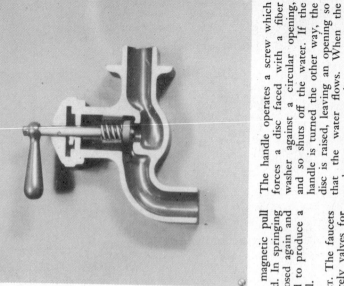

81 ELECTRIC DOOR BELL

82 COMPRESSION FAUCET

81. ELECTRIC DOOR BELL. When the button is pushed, the current flows through the green coils. This produces a magnetic pull which attracts the red iron bar, causing the clapper to strike the bell. As the red bar swings, it pulls the spring away from the screw contact and breaks the circuit. This stops the current so that there is no longer a magnetic pull and the bar is released. In springing back, the circuit is closed again and the process is repeated to produce a continuous ringing bell.

82. COMPRESSION FAUCET. The faucets in our houses are merely valves for opening and closing pipes. The compression faucet is the common type.

The handle operates a screw which forces a disc faced with a fiber washer against a circular opening, and so shuts off the water. If the handle is turned the other way, the disc is raised, leaving an opening so that the water flows. When the washer wears out, the connection is faulty, causing a leakage.

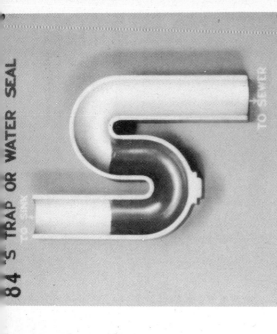

83 FULLER BALL FAUCET

84 "S" TRAP OR WATER SEAL

83. FULLER BALL FAUCET. In this model, a crank is used to open the valve instead of a screw. When crank is turned, stop washer A is forced back against water pressure and water rushes through the spigot. When crank is released, pressure of water in pipe closes stop A.

84. "S" TRAP OR WATER SEAL. Correct drainage in a house is very essential. A trap is a fixture placed in a waste pipe below the plumbing fixture to prevent gases from entering the house from the soil pipe or sewer. Advantage is taken of the fact that a gas will not force its way into water to a lower point. The water is represented by the green color. This type of trap is universally used.

215

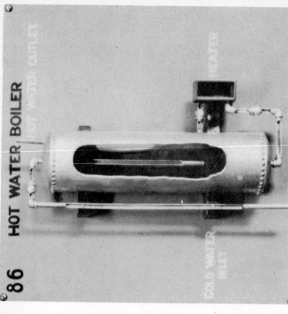

86   HOT WATER BOILER

COLD WATER INLET · HOT WATER OUTLET · HEATER

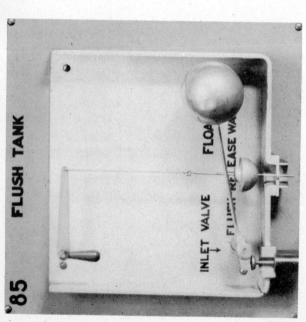

85   FLUSH TANK

INLET VALVE · FLOAT · FLUSH RELEASE WASHER

85. FLUSH TANK. As the handle is operated, the stop washer connected to it by a long rod is raised, opening a valve and forcing the water to leave the tank. See valve connections in faucets Nos. 82 and 83. The float ball descends with the water, thus opening the inlet valve to get a fresh supply of water. As water enters inlet valve, float rises, closing it to prevent overflow.

86. HOT WATER BOILER. The little red arrows will show you the course of the water through the boiler. It enters cold water inlet on left from street mains and flows through a pipe which reaches nearly to the bottom of the tank. From here it is led off to the heater where it flows through coils, is heated and returns to the tank nearer the top, leaving at hot water outlet. This causes a circulation which continues until all the water in the tank has passed through the heater and the whole tankful is hot.

87. PIPELESS FURNACE. Pipeless furnace is a device for circulating warm air through a house. Air is warmed by coming in contact with heated walls around fire box A, and rises through passages B. As warm air rises through the center of registers the cold air is automatically drawn downward through outer ring of registers into cold air duct C where it is warmed and returned, causing continual circulation of warm air through the house. An inlet pipe from out-of-doors may be used and regulated for desired fresh air.

88. STEAM OR HOT WATER HEATER. Heat generated in fire box A heats walls of furnace and surfaces going to smoke pipe, raising water in red sections to steam heat. Steam rising in steam dome is transmitted to steam pipes and radiators in building for heat desired.

217

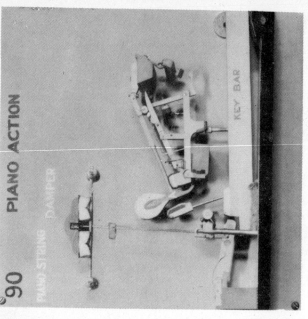

PIANO STRING DAMPER

KEY BAR

89. COAL BREAKER ROLLS. Connected with every commercial coal mine is a breaker plant for breaking and sorting the coal. Rolls of this type are placed in the top of the breaker building. The coal is led to the rollers and dumped in the top or hopper where it is broken by the rotation of the toothed rolls.

of key bar is pressed down, hammer A is caused to strike a quick blow on piano string, rebounding to allow string to vibrate. A quick rebound is caused by the elasticity of both the compressed felt in the hammer-head and the steel piano string. Under normal conditions of playing, the damper immediately touches string, causing vibrations to cease, thereby stop-

ping tone. When full volume of piano is needed, the loud pedal is pressed with the foot to cease operation of damper, allowing string to vibrate fully, giving large and sustained tones. The intricate mechanism is necessary to cause a quick return of hammer for rapid playing and to prevent resonance when repeating action is desired.

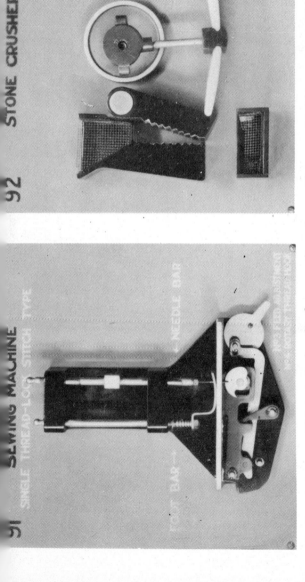

SINGLE THREAD—LOCK STITCH TYPE

FOOT BAR→

←NEEDLE BAR

NEAFEED BAR→
12 COTTON THREAD 1832

91. SEWING MACHINE. This is the lock stitch type machine. To show complete operation, material for sewing must operate through machine. As needle goes through material, foot bar presses foot down. When needle rises and draws thread up through material the foot rises and the toothed feeder under foot advances material the required distance for next stitch.

On first operation, when needle goes downward through material, the loop of thread is caught by revolving thread hook, which pulls thread taut in material. The repeating of this cycle produces a series of stitches continuously along a desired line. Desired length of stitch is regulated by feed adjustment.

92. STONE CRUSHER. This mechanism requires a very heavy pressure. Therefore a toggle joint is employed which is attached to the hinged jaw and is driven by an eccentric (See No. 23). In a toggle joint, two bars are joined together end to end but not in line, so that when a force is applied which tends to straighten out the arrangement, a great pressure is exerted, in

219

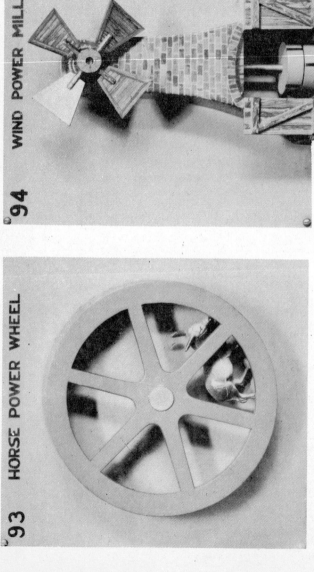

93. HORSE POWER WHEEL. The weight of the horse attempting to climb the side of the wheel causes the wheel to rotate. To the shaft of this wheel a belted pulley may be attached for transmission of power. This is a very early source of power but is still in use in isolated parts of the world.

this case, to the hinged jaws. A large stone or boulder is placed in the hopper and, as it moves by its own weight to the lower end of the jaws, it is crushed smaller and smaller till it falls through.

94. WIND POWER MILL. The velocity of the wind drives the wheel, which has blades that can be set at various angles in order to obtain a desired speed. The revolving shaft having one grinder attached to it works against the other. This early type was used for grinding grain.

95. CHINESE WHEEL FOR POWER. This wheel was first known as the "Chinese" wheel and was used to punish criminals and slaves. They were forced to tread the rungs in the wheel and so work out their punishment in labor. Then the wheel was equipped with a belt and pulley for transmitting power.

96. TREAD WHEEL FOR POWER. The power in this device is obtained by the action of animals traveling on the inclined plane. It was generally used in the early days in rural districts for churning and light work. Animals most generally adapted to this were dogs, goats, and sheep.

97. AUTOMOBILE ENGINE STARTER. This device, known as the "Bendix drive," is the starter. The starting motor is attached to the left end of shaft. As the starting pedal is pushed, the motor starts the shaft at a high speed, sending the small gear in mesh with the teeth on the fly wheel. The spring absorbs the starting shock. This starts

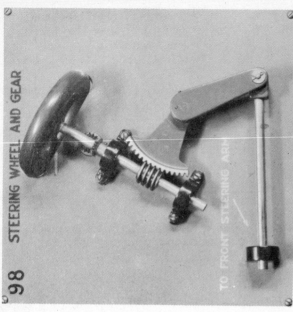

ENGINE FLY WHEEL

TO STARTER MOTOR

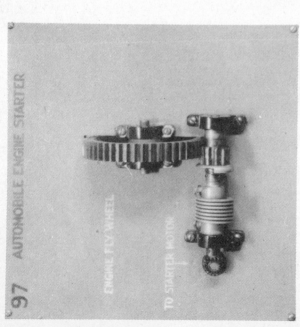

TO FRONT STEERING ARM

the engine (See No. 102), which soon picks up speed so that the fly wheel revolves faster than the small gear. This action causes the small gear, still meshed with it, to rotate on the threads of the starting shaft, now slowing down, and throws it back to its first position and out of mesh with the fly wheel.

98. STEERING WHEEL AND GEAR. The steering mechanism in this model is known as the worm and gear type. The action of the worm and gear is very strong. Use is made of a bell crank drive (See No. 10). The horizontal rod is connected to the steering arm on the front wheels.

99. UNIVERSAL JOINT. There are many forms of universal joints (See Section II). The advantage of this form is that it is noiseless in its action. The leather discs are very flexible and keep changing position. It is necessary to use a universal joint as the engine shaft and drive shaft are always out of line and every vibration of car changes angle.

VACUUM VALVE
SUPPLY PIPE
VENT TUBE
FLOAT
FLAPPER VALVE
AIR VALVE
DRAIN PLUG
LEAD TO CARBURETER

100. Auto vacuum tank. This shows a standard type of vacuum tank used to keep the carbureter supplied with liquid fuel all the time the engine is running, from the supply tank which is at a lower level than the carbureter. When a vacuum is caused in the tank by the piston action of engine (See No. 102), through supply tank, gasoline is sucked up from the supply line, entering through vacuum valve. As the tank is filled, the float rises, causing the lever arms attached above it to operate. This closes vacuum valve and opens air valve in vent tube, allowing air to enter from outside. As the engine runs, the gasoline within the lower part of the vacuum tank is supplied to the carbureter, and as it does so, the float falls with the gasoline level. When the level falls sufficiently, the little springs and the float operate the valves again and the operation is repeated.

101. Auto timer and distributor. In an internal combustion engine, it is very necessary that the igniting spark occur only in the cylinder that is ready to be fired and at the right time in the cycle of operations. The timer

223

101 AUTO TIMER AND DISTRIBUTOR

SPARK LEVER

RETARD

ADVANCE

102 INTERNAL COMBUSTION ENGINE FOUR CYCLE

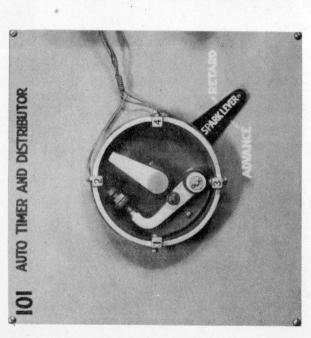

WATER

EXHAUST IN

EX

INTAKE

EX

WATER

VALVE RODS

CAM SHAFT

CRANK SHAFT

TIMING GEAR

OIL GAS

and distributor is the device which regulates this action. The revolving arm is rotated by cam shaft of the engine (See No. 102). As it revolves, it closes contact with the four terminals on the shell of timer, causing current to go to spark plugs on the engine and fire them in regular order. In this model the firing order is 1, 3, 4, 2. The other arm, called the breaker arm, breaks the current at each contact point as revolving arm travels against cam attached to it.

102. INTERNAL COMBUSTION ENGINE, FOUR CYCLE. This is called a four cycle, four cylinder motor because of the four steps in the process, repeating themselves in each one of the four cylinders. It is also called a combustion engine because the power is obtained by the rapid burning or combustion of a liquid, forming a gas which expands and exerts great pressure. The four steps in the process are the loading, compressing, firing, and exhausting or clearing. As the action is the same in all cylinders, the one on the right will serve as a good example.

Step 1. As the engine is started by

the starting device (See No. 97), the piston head starts downward and sucks a charge of vaporized gasoline in through the inlet valve from the carburetor (See No. 100 and No. 110). The piston is attached to the lower shaft, called the crank shaft, by the connecting rod. Connected to the crank shaft by means of gears is the cam shaft. The upper gear is four

times larger than the lower, therefore the upper or cam shaft rotates only once while the lower rotates four times. This regulates the next step.

Step 2. As the piston starts back, the inlet and exhaust valves are both closed by the action of the cam on the cam shaft, and the gas is compressed above the piston head.

Step 3. At the end of the up stroke,

the timer delivers current to the spark plug, making a spark which fires or explodes the compressed gas at the proper time causing the piston to go down. This is called the power stroke for it transmits a rotary motion through the crank shaft to the drive shaft of the car.

Step 4. At the end of the power stroke, the exhaust valve is opened

225

and the piston returning upward forces the used gas out through the valve into the muffler and into the air. Beginning at the right, the order of firing of the cylinders is 1, 3, 4, 2. The continuous explosion of gas causes the engine to heat up. Therefore a cooling system is needed, as shown in No. 103.

The circulating pump system shown in this model is most generally used today. As the water is heated it rises to the top of the water jacket and travels through this pipe into the top of the radiator. A cooling fan draws cold air in through the openings of the radiator and cools the water. The cool water is then drawn down through the radiator by gravity and by the pump rotor and enters the lower part of the water jacket to repeat its cooling action.

104. MULTIPLE DISC CLUTCH. Clutches were explained in No. 32. This type is a friction clutch. The shaft on the left is connected to the crank shaft of the engine (See No. 102). The two driving discs are mounted one on the crank shaft end, being the clutch

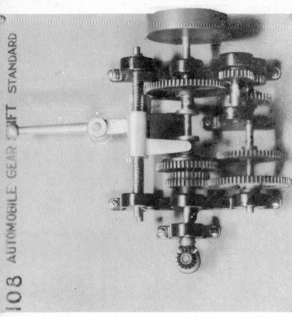

plate, and one on the drive shaft end. The clutch plate is fixed on a sleeve and slides on the crank shaft. The red and white disc on the right connects with the transmission (See No. 108). In front of the clutch plate are several discs mounted loosely on the crank shaft. When clutch pedal is pressed down, clutch plate and loosely mounted discs are parted, thereby breaking connection with the engine. When the clutch pedal is left in place the clutch plate gradually engages with the multiple discs, thereby starting the car. Multiple discs afford a smooth starting and less wear, because the fraction is distributed in all discs.

105. CONE CLUTCH. This is one of the earliest types of clutch used in automobiles. It is no longer used because the shock at starting was too great and the wear excessive.

106. AUTO DIFFERENTIAL. The differential in this model is the set of four miter gears in a bracket, connected with the shafts of the rear wheels. The purpose of this device is to allow one wheel to rotate with a different speed than the other if necessary, for example, in turning a corner. The

INDICATED LOAD

HEAT PIPE
BANJO
THROTTLE
CHOKE VALVE
HIGH SPEED JET
AIR VALVE
GASOLINE ADJUSTMENT

HEAT JACKET
AIR ADJ.
PRIMER ADJ.
FLOAT

small miter gears of the differential do not revolve when both wheels are running at the same speed but simply act as a lock between the driving sections of the two wheels. When there is a difference in speed, the two horizontal gears revolve on their own pinions and compensate for the difference. At the same time they keep the driving contact between the two sections of the axle.

107. INTERNAL AND EXTERNAL BRAKE. The working of foot and emergency brakes is shown in this model. When the foot brake lever is pressed down it operates the lever on the left and by toggle action (See No. 92), tightens the brake bands on outside of brake drum, retarding it according to the pressure exerted on the foot pedal. When the emergency lever is oper-

ated the same action on bottom of lever turns the eccentric cam, with powerful action, expanding the brake band on the inside of the drum with the same result.

108. AUTOMOBILE GEAR SHIFT, STANDARD. The upper revolving shaft is connected on the left end to the engine through the clutch. The right end of shaft is connected to the drive

shaft of the car which runs to the rear axle. This shaft is cut in two between the yellow and blue gears; each part revolves separately. The small or intermediate shaft carries reversing gear. The lower revolving or jack shaft carries four gears, all fixed. These mesh with upper gears to give the three speeds forward (low, intermediate, and high) and reverse. On the left, the two yellow gears always mesh. The upper shaft drives the lower, getting its power from the engine, reducing the speed of the lower shaft because the driving gear is smaller than the driven gear. On the right, the two lower red gears always mesh. When in *reverse* position, all red gears on right are in mesh. Follow motion of yellow gears and red gears to understand reverse action. When in *low* or *first* position, the green and red gears on the right mesh. The speed is low because a large gear on the upper shaft meshes with a much smaller one on the lower shaft, the lower gear now being the driver. In *second* or *intermediate* position, the two blue gears mesh, the speed of the upper shaft being the same as the lower, both gears being the same diameter. This speed is greater, however, than when in low. In *third* posi-tion or *high*, the yellow gear on the left locks inside of the blue gear. Now the speed transmitted is high because the driven gear is locked with the drive gear which runs at engine speed.

109. POWER MEASURING DYNAMOMETER. The purpose of this device is to measure the power required to drive a particular mechanism. It depends principally upon the action of a train of four bevel gears and a hoop-shaped frame. The two horizontal gears and the frame in which they are arranged revolve freely on the middle of the horizontal shaft, on which there are two vertical gears, the one on the right stationary, the other loose on the shaft. The vertical gears mesh with the horizontal gears. If a load is put on the gear loose on shaft at left, the power required to hold the hoop stationary is the power required to carry the load. This is measured by any device made to stop rotation of hoop which is attached to a recording arm which registers on scale.

110. GASOLINE CARBURETOR. The duty of the carburetor is to mix the fuel and air and insure the proper proportion of each before it is sent to the cylinder to be burned. Gasoline is supplied to the carburetor from the main supply tank by means of the vacuum tank (See No. 100). The carburetor converts the fuel into a vapor by mixing it with air.

Gasoline enters float chamber from vacuum tank (See No. 100), through needle valve attached by a lever on the float. When a sufficient supply is in, the float rises and valve closes. This float automatically keeps gasoline at proper level as in vacuum tank. Gasoline is then sucked into the mixing chamber in center by the action of engine pistons (See No. 102). It is mixed with air, admitted through air valve, which vaporizes it as it passes into distributor pipe or manifold for entrance into cylinders (See No. 102). When engine is running at a very high speed and additional gasoline is needed, it is drawn through the high speed jet. The throttle valve at top regulates the gas flow to the engine, thereby controlling its speed. The choke is used in starting when the motor is cold and the mixture will not explode properly. The air inlet is closed so that more gas enters the mixing chamber giving a richer mixture. The heat pipe leads from the exhaust manifold. Heat is drawn into the heat jacket around the carburetor which aids in vaporizing the gasoline, particularly in cold weather.

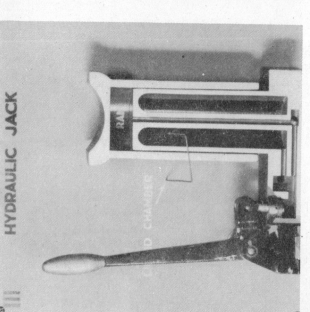

HYDRAULIC JACK

111. HYDRAULIC JACK. A hydraulic jack is very powerful. A small force will exert a tremendous lifting power. Pressure applied to the lever causes the valve A at opening of liquid chamber to open so that liquid is drawn from it and flows toward center cylinder. The lever returning in the opposite direction opens valve B into cylinder below ram allowing the liquid to rise in it and raise the ram. The great lifting power depends on the length of the lever and the size of the plunger attached to it. The longer the lever and smaller the plunger, the greater the force.

112 AUTO HORN KLAXON TYPE

112. AUTO HORN, KLAXON TYPE. This is the usual type automobile horn. The motor causes the vibrator or cam wheel to revolve against the button mounted on sound disc, causing it to vibrate. The greater the number of vibrations, the higher the pitch or tone. The horn or resonator amplifies the sound.

113 OLD OAKEN BUCKET

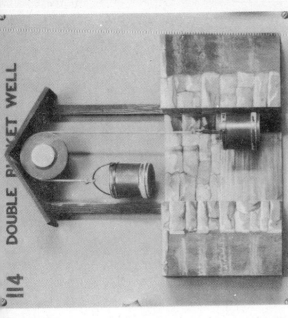

114 DOUBLE BUCKET WELL

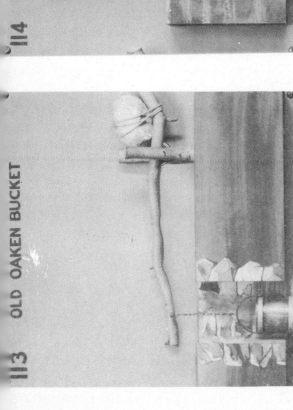

113. OLD OAKEN BUCKET. This is the first known method of raising water from a well of no considerable depth. Use is made of a lever of the first type (See first model on No. 2). The rock or counter balance attached to the boom assists in lifting the bucket because it equals about one-half of the weight to be raised.

114. DOUBLE BUCKET WELL. Another method for raising water makes use of the common pulley (See No. 25). The empty bucket is pulled down in order to raise the full one.

231

116 PENDULUM WATER LIFT

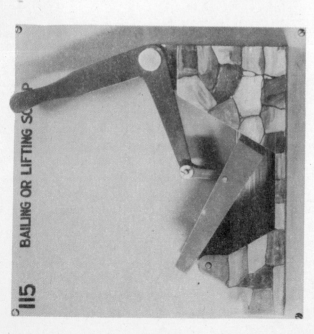

115 BAILING OR LIFTING SCOOP

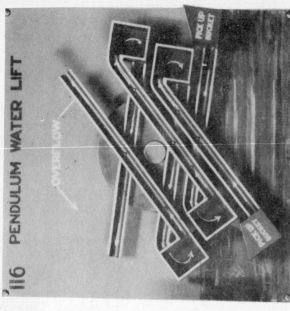

115. BAILING OR LIFTING SCOOP. This device is for raising water short distances. The scoop is connected by a rod to one end of the green elbow lever which has force applied at its other end.

116. PENDULUM WATER LIFT. This device for raising water is operated by hand or other power. By following the arrows leading from each pick-up bucket to the overflow it is easy to trace the action, the whole device oscillating on the center represented by red disc.

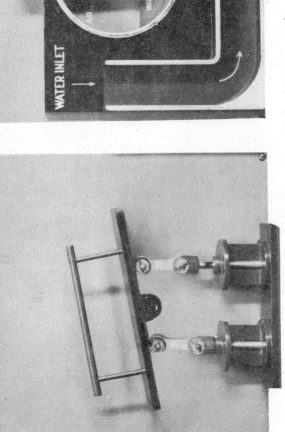

117. BALANCE PUMP. This type of pump was an early form, operated by a man swaying from right to left over the center of the bridge. Slaves and criminals were commonly used and so worked out their sentences in labor. The two plungers represent valve pumps.

118. HYDRAULIC RAM. This machine for raising water will furnish a supply of water at a high level. The alternate action of the two valves operated by the force of the moving water, allows the water to enter the air chamber. The valve on the right is kept open by its own weight until sufficient water has entered the inlet and forced it shut. As stop valve closes, the small valve is forced open and water enters the air chamber rising to a certain level with pressure that equalizes the air pressure. When the small valve closes again, the right-hand one opens. A constant upward stream into tank is obtained by the compressed air in chamber acting on surface of water.

119 FOURNEYRON TURBINE WATER WHEEL

120 WARREN TURBINE WATER WHEEL

119. FOURNEYRON TURBINE WATER WHEEL. As the water enters the holes in the center, it flows against the fixed guides or chutes. These direct the water against the buckets of the outer wheel, causing it to revolve.

The water then escapes through discharge.

120. WARREN TURBINE WATER WHEEL. In this type of turbine water wheel the position of fixed guides and revolving wheel is opposite to that in

No. 119. Water enters inlet at top and falling upon fixed guides on outside is directed upon center wheel, causing it to rotate. Water is discharged through holes at the center.

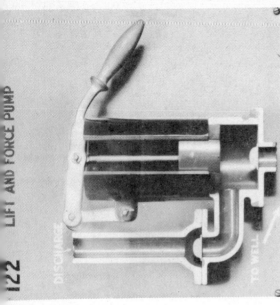

121. UNDERSHOT WATER WHEEL. The motion is caused by the water flowing under gate on left pushing against the wheel. The speed of the wheel is regulated by raising and lowering the gate valve, allowing more or less water to flow through.

122. LIFT AND FORCE PUMP. This is the ordinary force pump having two valves. The plunger is raised by the handle, causing valve A to rise, drawing water from low level into the pump chamber. On the descent of plunger, valve A closes and water is forced through valve B into discharge pipe at higher level. As handle is again raised, water in discharge pipe closes valve B.

124 VOLUTE TURBINE WATER WHEEL

DISCHARGE

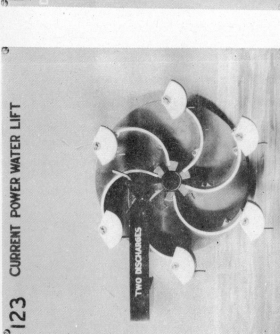

123 CURRENT POWER WATER LIFT

TWO DISCHARGES

123. CURRENT POWER WATER LIFT. This device is sometimes called a Persian wheel. It has a hollow shaft in the center and curved buckets, at the ends of which other forms of buckets are suspended. The motive power is supplied by the end buckets which turn as water strikes them and present a good driving surface. Their under surfaces offer no resistance because they travel in direction of water.

This is one of a few instances where the motive force also carries a load. As the wheel rotates, all buckets pick up water. The small buckets discharge water at the top after being tilted by a stationary pin and the curved buckets discharge water through the hollow shaft in center.

124. VOLUTE TURBINE WATER WHEEL. This type water motor is used for furnishing power. Water, entering at the inlet, flows around inside of gradually narrowing passage between vanes and outer shell, or casing, and causes vanes to rotate. Great pressure is exerted by the water seeking to escape. As the water escapes through the discharge at center, it is forced against the radial surfaces of the red propeller wheel and again exerts power on the drive shaft A.

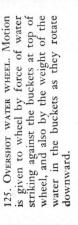

125. OVERSHOT WATER WHEEL. Motion is given to wheel by force of water striking against the buckets at top of wheel, and also by the weight of the water in the buckets as they rotate downward.

126. ARCHIMEDES SCREW. This machine is said to have been introduced by Archimedes. The motive power is supplied by the stream, rotating the green wheel. As spiral pipe, represented by glass, is rotated by the wheel, water runs in lower end seeking its level on the lower side of turn in pipe. This lower level advances with the spiral shape of pipe and water is automatically raised to the top and discharged. Note travel of water as represented by balls in bottom of each turn of coils.

128 STEERING WHEEL AND WINCH

TO RUDDER

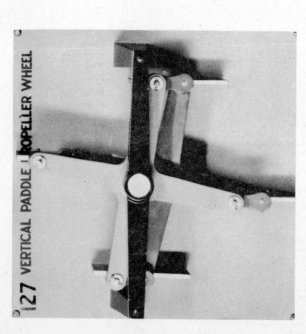

27 VERTICAL PADDLE PROPELLER WHEEL

127. VERTICAL PADDLE PROPELLER WHEEL. This is the most efficient type of paddle wheel. The green driver arms are the supports for the rotating paddles. The red arms are attached by crank arms to the green arms. The red driver is eccentric to the green driver. The rotating action of the two causes the paddles through the crank arm connections to be held always in a vertical position with their surfaces always meeting the water at right angles to their travel. This is the most efficient angle for driving.

128. STEERING WHEEL AND WINCH. Ordinary steering apparatus. On the shaft of the hand wheel is a barrel on which is wound a rope. The ends of the rope pass around guide pulleys and are attached to a lever or tiller on the top of the rudder. By turning the wheel in opposite directions, the rope will wind and unwind, pulling the lever in the direction the wheel is turned.

130 CLOCK ESCAPEMENT

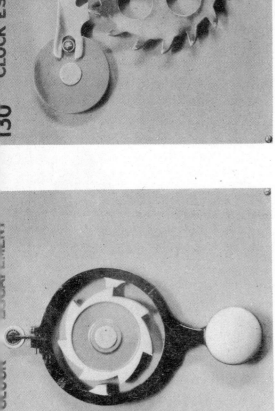

129. CLOCK ESCAPEMENT. An escapement is a combination in which a toothed wheel acts upon two distinct pieces or pallets attached to a reciprocating frame. The frame is so arranged that when one tooth escapes or ceases to drive its pallet, another tooth shall begin its action on another pallet. The object of an escapement in a clock or watch is to stop and then set in motion again, at regular intervals, every wheel in the entire train of mechanisms. This action causes the familiar tick of a clock and watch. The rotating toothed wheel is the driver and gives a swinging or oscillating motion to the driven member. This type of escapement was used on the first clock movements when whole works were made of wood.

130. CLOCK ESCAPEMENT. In this model, the arm which holds the pallets is guided by a pin fastened to the red disc. The wheel is kept from escaping or making a continuous rotary movement by the alternate action of the pallets entering and retiring from between the teeth of the escape wheel.

239

132 WATCH ESCAPEMENT

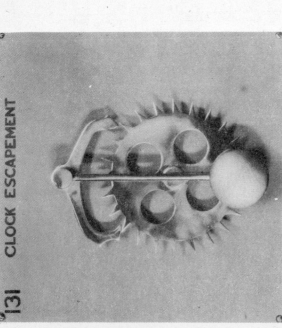

131 CLOCK ESCAPEMENT

131. CLOCK ESCAPEMENT. The Seth Thomas clock exhibit (See No. 135) makes use of a type of clock escapement very similar to this, the only difference being a slight change in the shape of the pallets. The escape wheel, which turns in a clockwise direction, is supplied with long, pointed teeth. As it turns, the pallets alternately come in contact with the teeth, and cause the pendulum to swing.

132. WATCH ESCAPEMENT. The escapement in watches operates on the same principle as that in clocks, though a balance wheel is used instead of a pendulum. The anchor-shaped piece with two horns is called the pallet. First one horn of the pallet, then the other, locks with the teeth of the escape wheel as it revolves. The unlocking is accomplished by a lever attached to the pallet. The action of this lever is controlled by a balance wheel which gets its action from the coiled spring often called a "hair spring." The lever is alternately engaged and released with the balance wheel by means of the small pin. Not only ingenuity, but the greatest accuracy and delicacy, is required of the machinery used in the art of watchmaking.

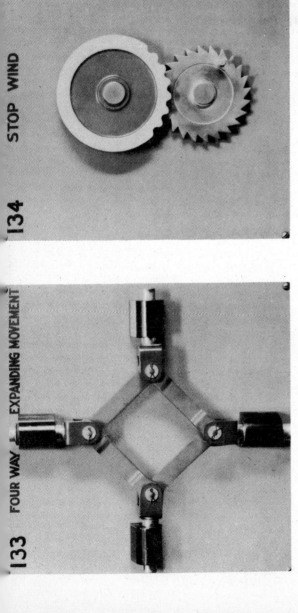

133 FOUR WAY EXPANDING MOVEMENT

134 STOP WIND

133. FOUR-WAY EXPANDING MOVEMENT. When motion is given to any one of the arms, the remaining three move the same distance.

134. STOP WIND. As the disc carrying ratchet teeth revolves, the pin attached to it carries the upper disc forward the distance of one tooth. After the last tooth is advanced, the pin rests against the outer edge of red disc and is held in that position against rotation. Flyback of red wheel represents running down of spring. This movement is used in watches to prevent overwinding the spring which causes breakage.

BALING PRESS

136

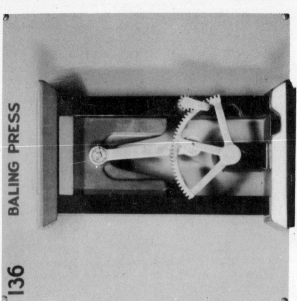

135. SETH THOMAS CLOCK.

136. BALING PRESS. This hand press is used for pressing cotton, waste paper and other material into a baling form to be tied for handling. The motion given through the hand crank is trans-mitted to the press by means of the toothed sector and rod connected with it at a greatly multiplied power.

OLDEST TYPE

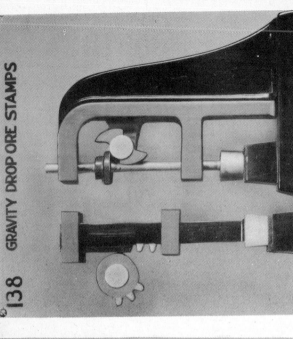

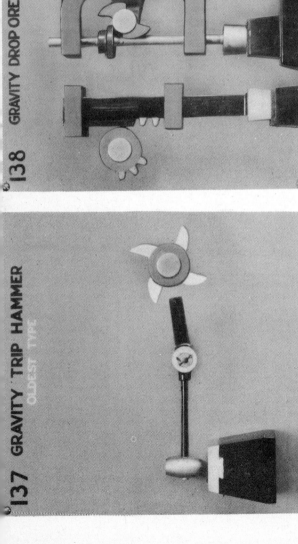

137. GRAVITY TRIP HAMMER. The hammer is lifted by the revolution of the toothed cam, four times to each revolution. Force of blow depends upon weight and length of drop of hammer head. This is one of the first types of power-driven forging hammers.

138. GRAVITY DROP ORE STAMPS. In the left-hand model, sharp falls of the vertical rod are derived from the mutilated rotating wheel or pinion. This pinion acts upon the teeth in the rod and raises it until all teeth have meshed; then the rod falls.

In the other model, the rod is raised by the action of the revolving cam against the green lift collar. These are used for crushing rock to extract the ore and are generally mounted in gangs, having a large number in line.

243

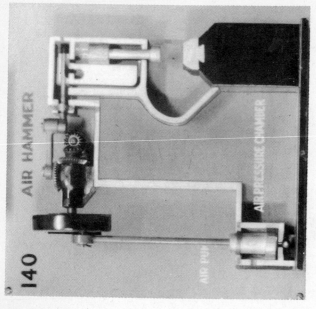

139 TYPEWRITER KEY-BAR

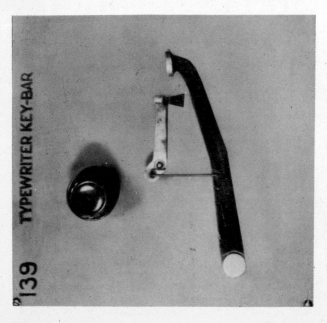

140 AIR HAMMER

AIR PUMP

AIR PRESSURE CHAMBER

139. TYPEWRITER KEY BAR. When key bar is struck by operator, the type bar is raised quickly by the connecting rod, striking the platen or roller and making the impression upon the paper through the typewriter ribbon which is held in front of platen. Recovery to original position is made by action of a tension spring.

140. AIR HAMMER. The head of this hammer is attached to a piston A, and is made to work in cylinder B, by the intermittent releasing of compressed air into the cylinder above and below by the slide-valve on top. The air is supplied from the air pressure chamber into which it has been forced by the air pump. When pump piston C is in up position, air enters through D and is compressed as piston descends through valve in bottom of cylinder. The air pump is driven by a crank attached to the black revolving disc on driving shaft. This type of hammer is used for heavy duty forging and can also be operated by steam pressure.

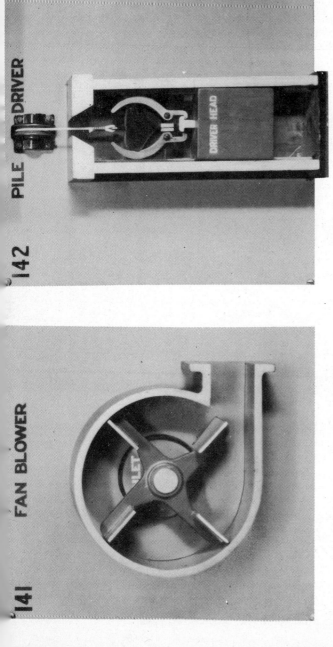

141 FAN BLOWER

PILE DRIVER

142

141. Fan blower. This is the well known type of fan blower used for forced air draught on ventilating systems. By the revolution of the central shaft and attached fan blades, air is drawn in at the center of the casing through the inlet and forced out un-

der pressure through the spout.

142. Pile driver. The earliest form of pile driver. The driver head is lifted by hooks to a sufficient height. Then the hooks are released by pressure of hook arms against the sides of the

slot in the top of the frame, releasing the driver head. Its driving power depends on the weight of the driver and the height of drop since the force accumulates as the driver falls.

144 TOGGLE PUNCH

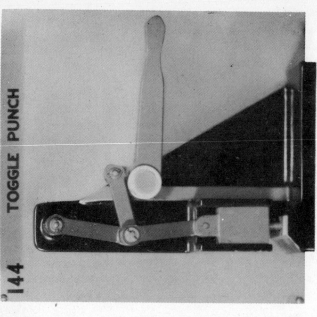

143 ROTARY CONVEYOR

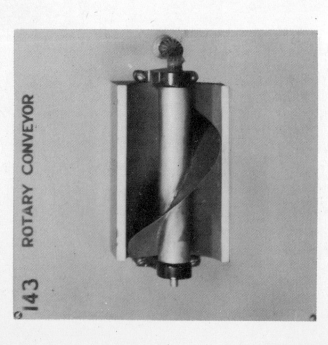

143. ROTARY CONVEYOR. A spiral blade is attached to the driving shaft so that as it rotates, the material being conveyed is pushed forward by the face of the blade in the direction of the arrow.

144. TOGGLE PUNCH. The hand lever working upon the joint or horizontal connecting link through short center leverage at the end of handle exerts a terrific power on punch through toggle action, as explained in No. 92.

145. FIRST STEAM ENGINE. Date, 130 B.C. Heron's engine is now regarded as the first steam engine. Steam is generated in the lower vessel, or boiler, and conducted into the globular vessel above by two bent tubes. These tubes also serve as pivots on which the globe revolves. Its rotation is caused by the steam escaping from the four bent arms and its direction is opposite to that of the steam travel.

146. TRUNK TYPE ENGINE. This is a simple form of the early type of trunk or atmospheric engine. Steam is admitted in bottom part of cylinder A through part B, causing piston to rise. At end of up stroke a jet of cold water is thrown into cylinder A through D, cooling steam and causing vacuum to draw piston down. The inertia stored in heavy fly wheel on shaft during up stroke of piston, causes crank C to travel over center for down stroke. It is now obsolete but was generally used before the introduction of the slide valve engine (See No. 154).

147 OSCILLATING CYLINDER ENGINE

NOTE PORTS
TOP AND BOTTOM

148 OSCILLATING PISTON ENGINE

BOILER PRESSURE

EXHAUST PORT

147. OSCILLATING CYLINDER ENGINE. This engine is not a very efficient type. The cylinder is pivoted at its center to the engine frame, turning on pivot with an oscillating motion. Note the upper and lower parts in the back face of the cylinder to admit and exhaust the steam. As piston travels up, steam pressure is admitted through lower right port and exhausts through upper left port. As piston descends, steam is admitted through upper right port and exhausted through lower left port. The action of the piston rod drives the fly wheel to which it is attached by means of a crank. The inertia of the fly wheel carries the crank over the centers.

148. OSCILLATING PISTON ENGINE. Steam enters at the top from the boiler and is admitted into the piston chamber A through steam ports by the action of the slide valve B. The steam alternately strikes against the sides of the oscillating piston and passes through the exhaust port into the atmosphere. The crank C is attached to the piston shaft at bottom and is connected by a pitman rod D to the fly wheel. The crank pin operating in slot of valve rod E strikes the end of slot alternately and moves the upright valve arm F causing slide valve B to open and close steam ports.

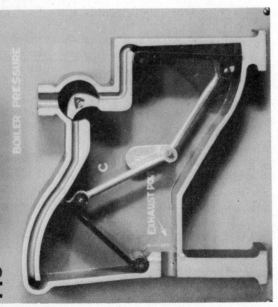

BOILER PRESSURE

EXHAUST PORT

EXHAUST PIPE

BOILER PRESSURE

A

149. DOUBLE QUADRANT STEAM ENGINE. This model is called the double quadrant steam engine because the two piston rods are attached to arms, which move in a quadrant or area equal to one quarter of a circle. Steam enters from the boiler at the top. The inlet valve A is attached to crank B on under side by a cam. Valve A allows steam to enter ports moving each piston arm alternately in a quadrant, turning crank B. On return stroke of red arms steam escapes into interior chamber C and through exhaust port into the air.

150. ROTARY ENGINE OR PUMP. This is a very common form of rotary engine or pump. Steam entering at inlet on right exerts a pressure on the eccentric piston rotating in center of cylinder, causing it to revolve until the longest point from the center, indicated by arrow, passes the outlet, where steam passes into atmosphere. The slide A follows the piston ard acts as a barrier against high pressure steam entering inlet. When used as a pump, piston is driven by power, water enters at boiler pressure inlet and is forced out exhaust port as piston revolves.

151 ELIPTICAL GEAR ENGINE OR PUMP

BOILER PRESSURE

EXHAUST PIPE

152 VERTICAL ENGINE MARINE TYPE

BOILER PRESSURE   EXHAUST PART

151. ELLIPTICAL GEAR ENGINE OR PUMP. Elliptical gears were explained briefly in No. 67. Steam enters at top from boiler and by exerting pressure on the arms of gears, the pistons rotate. As arms pass exhaust pipe entrance in turn, steam passes into the air. When used as a pump, the action is the same as in No. 150.

152. VERTICAL ENGINE. MARINE TYPE. The slide valve which regulates the flow of steam into the piston chamber, is operated in this engine by a cam mounted on drive shaft. It is sometimes called a cam valve engine. The piston rod being driven by the force of the steam in cylinder turns the crank shaft attached to the cam causing it to revolve as in No. 154.

153. SPRING TYPE ENGINE GOVERNOR. A governor is a device to regulate the speed of an engine and was invented by James Watt. In this type the balls are attached to springs, having their upper ends fastened to a collar fixed on the central shaft and their lower ends fastened to a collar on a sliding sleeve. The springs are of such a tension that they will remain in one position for a required speed of the engine. When the engine exceeds this speed the balls are thrown outward by centrifugal force raising the sleeve stem and closing the valve so that the steam pressure is shut off. This keeps the speed of the engine constant.

154. HORIZONTAL SLIDE VALVE ENGINE. This is the well known type of reciprocating slide valve engine in universal use. Steam, entering steam ports alternately by action of sliding valve, operates piston in cylinder. Attached to the piston rod is a crank and crank arm which drives the fly wheel. An eccentric on drive shaft operates tie sliding valve through eccentric rod.

251

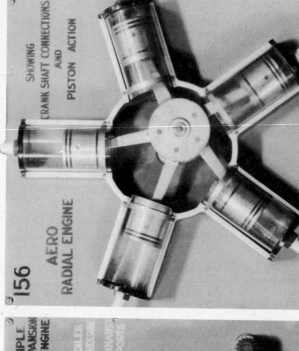

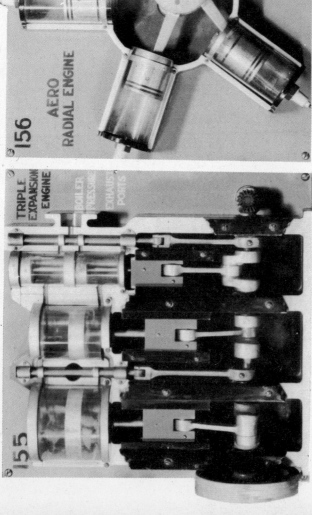

155. TRIPLE EXPANSION ENGINE. Steam enters the cylinder on the right at high pressure causing piston rod to operate in regular way as in No. 152 and No. 154. After it performs its work, it is exhausted into low pressure cylinder in center and in turn into third low pressure cylinder on left. From here it is exhausted into atmosphere.

156. AERO RADIAL ENGINE. This is a radial engine of the airplane type. The vertical connecting rod with a disc type head is directly attached to the drive shaft crank A. This rod revolves completely with the crank.

Note how the other four rods are connected to the disc. They are not rigid but oscillate as the disc turns. Valve actions and ignition are omitted as they are fully shown in Auto engine model No. 102. Firing rotation is every other cylinder in the 5, 7, or 9 cylinder types of engines.

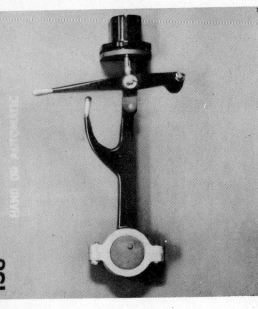

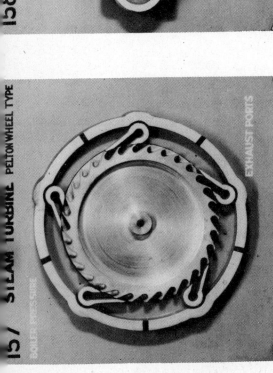

157. STEAM TURBINE. Pelton wheel type. High pressure steam entering five steam inlets drives against the outside surface of the wheel making it revolve at a high speed. The speed is regulated by the opening of the steam port or inlet. Steam escapes through exhaust ports in casing.

158. VALVE GEAR. HAND OR AUTOMATIC. This is the first type used on stationary slide valve engines. Horizontal arm or handle is designed to be disconnected by hand from green head of valve rod. If this is done, vertical arm controls valve stem by hand operation. This change is necessary to enable the engineer to stop his engine off center or in a position where it will start again. This is done by watching crank shaft and closing both steam ports by action of vertical lever causing engine to stop in that position. Rods are then connected for automatic starting.

253

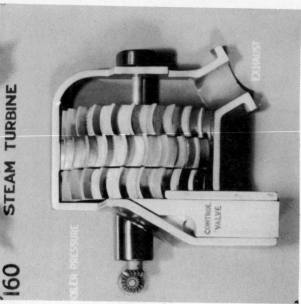

160 STEAM TURBINE

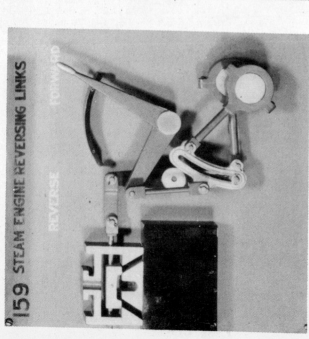

159 STEAM ENGINE REVERSING LINKS

159. STEAM ENGINE REVERSING LINKS. This is another type of valve gear called the reversing type and is most commonly used on locomotives. As you will note in the automatic action of this model, when the hand lever is thrown forward or backward it changes the position of the slide valve through action of slotted link motion, admitting steam in either end of cylinder as desired in order to start the engine forward or backward.

160. STEAM TURBINE. This type of turbine is an improvement over No. 157. Through the multiple arrangement of the bucket wheels, steam enters through control valve striking first wheel fixed to shaft causing both to rotate. As this steam passes through, it strikes the stationary wheel in center and is deflected so that it strikes the third wheel, also fixed to shaft, again furnishing power to drive shaft.

INDEX